DEDICATED TO

Tiffany, Samira,

Jeannine, Celene,

& Ameer.

IMPRESSIONS
published by RaMar Publishing
Lake Oswego, Oregon

© 1997 by Sar Ramadan
International Standard Book Number: 0-9659111-0-1

Impressions

SAR RAMADAN

RAMAR PUBLISHING ☼ LAKE OSWEGO, OREGON

I L L U S T R A T I O N S

The artistic illustrations contained in this book, as well as the book's cover, are the work of the gifted artist Blaise Jette. He is a free lance illustrator who lives in Portland Oregon. Blaise was born and raised in Montana and received a Bachelor of Fine Arts in Illustrations from the Arts Center College of Design in Pasadena, California.

I am delighted to have had the pleasure of assigning the art work to Blaise, and grateful for his enthusiasm, commitment and the beautiful illustrations he created.

Impressions (Book cover)
War In Ismailia
Wind Passion
Transiency Of Self
From Colossus To Nothingness

S A R   R A M A D A N

ACKNOWLEDGMENT

This book could not have seen the light without the moral support, insightful suggestions and much needed advice from my editor Colleen Watkins. Her friendship, encouragement, guidance, and sense of humor have motivated me to see the book through all the processes — from the first draft through printing.

The creative book-layout contributed by Laura Zugzda whose artistry, passion and enthusiasm provided the final touches to the book.

I am also appreciative for the suggestions, final-draft edits and support of my co-workers David Eastman and Sandra Philbrook at IMS Corporation, as well as, Myrna Oakley, Dorothy Deline, Linda West of Marylhurst College in Oregon.

Finally, I would like to thank my long-time friends everywhere; who held mirrors to my face and let me see reflections of myself, who, by their mere presence in my life, allowed me to see other angles of reality, and other aspects of human experience: Moustafa Soliman, Hammam Shaheen, Wafeek Ramadan in Egypt, Sivasti Anastathiado in Greece, Caroline Pichot and JeanPaul Franco in France, Bill Johnson, Roger Kuhn, Jeacques Galet, Theresa Burton in Boston, Sheri Mason in Washington D.C., Enery Martinez in Martinique, Takashi Nakamura and Noriko Funahashi in Tokyo, Alan Beauchamp, and Rhonda Smith-Sanchez Windsurfing Champion (and my instructor) in Oregon.

Sar Ramadan was born in Egypt in the midst of German air raids on his home town, Ismailia, during the second world war. The town is mid-point of the Suez Canal. It was occupied by British troops and became an international enclave in the Egyptian desert. Its multi-cultural mix, and sizable Greek and French communities provided insights and opportunities for an inquiring mind to explore. Ramadan learned French, English and Arabic, and has written short stories in both English and Arabic. His essentially analytical mind has recently exposed itself to the delights of poetry writing as another means for self-expression.

He studied business at Ain Shams University in Cairo, and upon graduation joined the nationalized Suez Canal Authority. Then, disillusioned by on-going warfare between the Arabs and Israelis, he emigrated to the United States in 1970, and subsequently completed two graduate degrees in business from University of New Haven and Harvard University.

Ramadan has lived, worked, and engaged in business in the Middle-East, Europe, and both the east and west coasts of the United States. He has traveled extensively for business and pleasure in Europe, Japan, South-East Asia, and South America; studied Greek, Existentialist and Buddhist philosophies and literature as a hobby. He is also an avid windsurfer.

He currently lives in Oregon where he is Chief Financial Officer for IMS Corporation, and lectures at Marylhurst College's Graduate School of Business.

Introduction

*"The struggle... is itself enough to fulfill the heart of man.
One must believe that Sisyphus is happy."*

LE MYTHE DE SISYPHE (1942)
ALBERT CAMUS (1913 - 1960)

The myth of Sisyphus is a tale of a man accused of stealing secrets of the Gods. The Gods condemned him to death, but as a price for returning to life, they ordained that he ceaselessly roll a huge rock to the top of a mountain. Each time he reached the top, the rock fell back of its own weight. The Gods reasoned that a futile and hopeless struggle was the ultimate punishment.

Camus' belief that Sisyphus is happy is an appropriately optimistic note upon which to introduce Sar's thought-provoking collections of IMPRESSIONS in which he pursues his own physical and psychological struggles to uncover unknowns, and realize unforeseeable horizons.

If the journey is indeed the prize, then we all win, as we share in the excursions of discovery which have been meticulously painted for our visual enjoyment and philosophical consideration. We follow the restless peregrinations of a passionate soul in search of the meaning of this absurdity known as life; of one who has *"... laid [his] heart open to the benign indifference of the universe."* (Camus) And we are often surprised at the intensity of insights provided en route.

This mini-saga speaks to the historical documentation of like crusaders — from Gilgamesh to Luke Skywalker — seeking a solution to the ultimate elusiveness, and journeying afar, in the inevitable rites of passage that lead directly, if painfully and circuitously, to the essence of Oneself. For those who relish the comfort of armchair travel, or who are stimulated by considered, critical philosophical commentary, I bid you Bon Voyage.

The journey I undertook in editing the manuscript, and guiding Sar through the demanding literary aspects of this small opus, has likewise provided many challenges and rewards — not the least of which is the discovery of a dynamic, quietly-determined and multi-faceted friend. Thank you Sar. It's been a pleasure.

COLLEEN J. WATKINS

Odyssey

BANDON BY-THE-SEA

Impressions

STILL-LIFE PAINTINGS OF LIVING

Finally, after so many blazing years, I find time and space to rekindle strong feelings, revive deep thoughts, and repaint colorful impressions for myself... I wonder what is magical about this moment? What is the mystique that surrounds me in this space?

I simply do not know.

For years, I have reflected, replayed, and savored these Impressions in the darkness of my mind. I have kept them all buried deep within my soul. I have treasured and separated them from everybody and everything. In my heart I knew: one day they would come alive and breathe again; one day they would emerge like autumn leaves dressed in most vivid colors.

Suddenly, the day has come: unexpected, unannounced. The urge is so compelling, the drive so strong that I can't tarry any longer. The images are flashing rapidly; emotions are flooding through. Nothing can stop this tidal wave of revelations. There is much to express, reveal and unleash within the short limits of one's life. I know not how much time I have, but I know one thing for certain, and that is the need to begin.

These Impressions are not simply photographs of reality, they are like paintings — passionate reflections and interpretations of my memory. They are neither composed of new colors, nor do they emanate from any philosophical breakthrough. They are my earnest attempts to comprehend, appreciate, and express myself.

When a painter portrays his impression of reality, he reacts to and reflects something that already exists. He sees something unusual or

beautiful, feels something joyful or painful — something that grips
him, steers his emotions, provokes his deepest thoughts. Finally, he is
compelled to create an impression of what grips him, with passion
and honesty.

In the end, these impressions contain the person along with the
feelings and the thoughts, all merged with the subject of the painting.
From this fusion comes something unique; its artistic value can only be
determined by the way in which others react to it. Only others can give
these creations meaning and value: by reflecting upon them, and allowing
them to influence their reality, even in the smallest way.

Reality is dynamic, a complex and forever changing form. My
vantage point influences my perception. I find it essential therefore to
move around and look at reality from different angles, and in varying
degrees of light and shade. This is something I must do with the hope
of gathering a more complete impression of what reality is. Without this
process, my vision would be limited, my comprehension incomplete, and
my impressions deceptive.

I have traveled near and far, at times wondering where the road was
leading me. I have followed the sun, felt the strong wind upon my face,
roamed the beaches and the back streets of this planet, forever
questioning why I came to be. I have sat near many fountains in strange
and lonely places, and let the sun warm my worn out soul in my search
for meaning. I found some comfort and peace in horizons where the sea
and the sky are in perfect unity and total harmony. I walked through life
with eyes wide open, with a soul made tender from pain, in awe of
human resilience, and with wonder at the beauty and frailty of life. I
made sincere attempts to understand great philosophers, sensitive poets,
and marvelous "ordinary" people, as they endure and enjoy life.

Out of my joyous and painful journeys, these impressions came
to life. Everywhere I found a scene, a context, a culture. Often, I was

struck by a thought, or influenced by a place that urged me to consider, discover, and seek validation for everything — even myself.

Granted, I know little with absolute certainty. The bounds of my comprehension, and time, do not allow me to know the full truth, nor arrive at near complete answers. I can think, see, feel, and paint word pictures, but I have to acknowledge my profound limitations. Reality does not stay still long enough for me to capture it in focus. My impressions are still-life paintings of living and forever dynamic images. Undoubtedly there are dimensions I still cannot see, secrets I cannot know, riddles I cannot solve.

My journey continues. Every day is a new discovery, and every new discovery is nothing but a small drop in the sea of reality. I press on, searching, discovering and attempting to comprehend even the incomprehensible. I must carry this torch to the last breath, and leave it flaming, glowing and alive.

WAR IN ISMALIA

War

A MANGO TREE IN THE INFERNO

It is a sunny morning in June. I sit in a small roof garden sipping my first cup of herbal tea. The sun feels warm and comforting. I close my eyes, take a deep breath and listen to the soothing street sounds: soft noises of children playing; street vendors shouting and peddling their onion, zucchini and watermelon; the nearby Greek church bells ringing softly... all are familiar and reassuring sounds. Aunt Farida brings out a tray full of her delicious cookies. She lays it gently on a small table beside me, with a mother's all-knowing smile. Her kind hazel eyes sparkle, her familiar tanned face radiates as she puts her warm hand on my shoulder and says, "Enjoy." I am grateful for this affectionate, kindhearted, hardworking woman who raised me.

A cool summer breeze carries with it a faint fragrance of jasmine, making me relaxed... almost lazy. Tropical trees around town are beginning to flame with familiar red flowers, a long awaited sign ushering-in the beloved summer. For me, in my early twenties, this is when real life begins. I have an intense dislike of winter, and am somewhat indifferent to spring or autumn. I reserve all my passion for summer: long swims in the warm waters of Lake Timsah, soccer games on the sandy beach, parties that last till dawn, pretty European girls, and moonlight sailing on the Lake. My heart worships the sun; I bask in its glory and let it warm my soul, and like a true Aquarian, I adore the sea... I dive into its maternal embrace and let it wash away all my sorrows.

From my aunt's roof garden, the view of Ismailia with its clusters of yellow-washed houses and their red-tiled roofs is particularly peaceful this morning. Women are hanging clothes to dry in the breezy sunshine. Mango trees are finally bearing fruit. The Mediterranean sky is bright blue without a trace of clouds. I stretch and smile, warming my bare legs in the bright morning sun as I continue to savor my first cup of tea. Life is good…

Suddenly, a thunderous explosion shakes my small town, shattering glass windows and reverberating violently in all directions. A fighter jet shrieks in front of my eyes, flying low over the roof tops. I jerk straight up in my deck chair, breathless, and with heart pounding. My inner-time suddenly elongates as I watch the events in a slow-motion. The jet skims over the city, the sunshine reflects on its silvery wings and the color of an inferno blazes from its tail. I hear the sounds of heavy gunfire all around me. Before I am able to collect my thoughts, another jet passes over my head with a blustering noise, at lightning speed.

"It is war once again," I whisper to myself in disbelief.

Back then, Ismailia was a beautiful and unusual town, compared to the rest of Egypt, and boasted a population of several hundred thousand people. The French, who ran the Suez Canal for decades, designed and built Ismailia in contemporary 19th century style. They planned it with broad avenues, tree-lined squares, a gridiron street plan surrounded by parks and gardens on three sides. They wanted Ismailia to become *"A little Paris away from Paris."*

Ismailia was founded in 1863 and named after the Khedive, Ismail Pasha, who ruled Egypt at that time. Ismail was a man known for his extravagant tastes, reckless spending, and legendary love affairs. His father, Khedive Said, had authorized a concession to his friend Ferdinand de Lesseps (a French diplomat, administrator and public relations man) to build the Suez Canal. Lesseps founded an international Suez Canal company, half financed by the French Public and half by international investors. The construction started in 1859 and ended ten years later.

The ancient Egyptians initiated the idea of connecting the Red Sea and the Mediterranean, however, they connected them via a branch of the River Nile. In the 19th century, a new idea was advanced by French engineers and promoted by Lesseps: to connect the two seas by digging a straight line running from Port Said in the north to the port of Suez in the south. The canal was connected to Lake Timsah from both ends, making it a part of the navigation path. The Suez canal finally formed a distinctive dividing line between Africa and Asia.

The project took ten long and arduous years. Thousands of Egyptian laborers dug the one-hundred-mile canal with their bare hands, using only the most primitive tools. It was not only back-breaking work — it was virtual slavery. Under the savage desert sun, through the wild and blinding sand-storms, Turkish foremen cracked their whips to drive the Egyptian workers. The men were tired, thirsty, sun-stricken, and sand blasted after working long hours to beat the schedule established by the French. The thirsty desert sand drank their sweat and blood, and thousands died and were buried in the same sand dunes they had just dug.

My grandfather migrated from upper Egypt along with the thousands of workers who came to dig the Suez canal. He lived long enough to witness the celebrations of its opening. I never saw him, never knew how and when he died. I only saw pictures of Grandfather: he had thick dark hair and a curled mustache that rivaled that of the Khedive. He looked strong, handsome and proud, with piercing black eyes that showed a good deal of toughness and a hint of sadness.

Khedive Ismail selected a spot beside Lake Timsah, midway between the Mediterranean and the Red Sea, to hold the lavish official opening of the Suez Canal in 1869. For this occasion, he built an elaborate palace with lush, manicured gardens, landscaped with beautiful shrubs of jasmine and mango plants. He held a special gala attended by royalty from around the world. The palace was said to be occupied for only a single night. Later on, it became surrounded by Mediterranean yellow-stone villas with red-tile roofs, for French officials who ran the canal. The company added small marinas on the lake with sailing, rowing, riding and tennis clubs, as well as a large hospital, exclusively for its employees.

Ismailia stretches west in lush profusion, on the African side of the Suez. Its parks, gardens and mango trees are irrigated by a branch of the river Nile that reaches from the Nile delta and ends in Lake Timsah. On the opposite side lies the deadly Sinai Desert: the gateway to Asia, the battlefield where Egyptians and Jews have foolishly fought and killed each other since the times of Ramses and Moses.

Lush gardens and mango trees flourishing on the west side of the canal and dry, sandy and barren desert to the east provide a dramatic contrast. Only a narrow ribbon of water separates the two worlds. This is a fitting metaphor for life and death, a symbolic reminder that life is moist, colorful and growing, while death is a barren and bleak nothingness.

Ships passing through the narrow Suez Canal make the scene even more bizarre. Huge tankers and oceanliners hoisting flags of every nation, navigate through the yellow sand dunes on one side, and the lush green gardens on the other. The scene seems unreal—like a collage of unrelated pictures thrown together by an artist with a sardonic sense of humor.

The people who once lived in Ismailia were a melange of cultures and nationalities: French bureaucrats who ran the canal, British troops who had occupied the area since the 1880's, Greeks and Italians who fled the devastation of the world wars in Europe and became the skilled laborers and small shop owners, and Egyptians who lived with, worked with, loved and hated all of them. Each influenced the other in every imaginable way, from language to culture, to habits, to outlook. The children of this extraordinary town became products of all these cultures, products of contradicting religions, languages, customs, and views of the world.

This was the town of my birth, Ismailia — the town that cradled my childhood dreams, my small triumphs, my follies, my laughter and my tears. Here I lost my younger sister to a simple fever when she was only four, and lost my chain-smoking father to lung cancer, when he was only forty. This is the place where I had to face the absurd realities of life earlier than I cared to; the place that shaped the person I later became. I attended an English preschool where Christian, Moslem and Jewish children sat side-by-side and listened to Mrs. King our English teacher reading her favorite poems.

During a few quiet years of Ismailia's history, from the late forties to the mid-sixties, the diverse cultures and related stigmas watered each other down to a level of mutual acceptance. There were too many different religions, too many silly traditions, and too many ridiculous customs, we thought. We, the children of Ismailia, had chosen either to ignore them or to laugh about their absurdity. We came to understand that all these barriers were superficial and meaningless, because we had been exposed to too much variety to believe in one thing or the other. We proved we could live with one another in peace and in harmony, and we discovered that neither good nor evil depends on nationality or religion. We understood that we were all humans sharing the same destiny and facing the same limitations of life.

The strategic nature of the Suez Canal, as the key route for transporting Middle East oil to the western world, made the area a hot-bed of contention between the international super powers. They all maneuvered and used political, economic and military force to control the canal one way or the other. Ismailia, being at the center of the canal, at times became the headquarters: for British troops in the entire Middle East until 1954, for the French Suez Canal Company until it was nationalized in 1956, and for the Egyptian Army throughout the War of Attrition with Israel from 1967 to 1973.

To make matters worse, the politicians, the religious fanatics, and the warmongers, on both sides of the Middle East conflict, continually brought war to the region. Every few years this narrow-mindedness, combined with the designs of the super powers, managed to create misery for my unique and beautiful town. Each time we started to feel safe, to live-and-let-live, the bombs came again to blow apart our peaceful co-existence.

The politicians on one hand, and the fanatics on the other were a deadly combination that existed on both sides of the Middle East conflict. They fed on each other in a vicious cycle. The politicians played on the fanatics' beliefs, to manipulate them to back their political ambitions. The fanatics, encouraged by the politicians, continued to spread their myopic vision and archaic teachings that go back to the Dark Ages. The absurd result was war, in which each side was fighting against "the enemies of God." Each side was convinced of the "justice" of its cause. The super powers — be they the British, French, Americans or Russians — deliberately fed the fires and kept the region in a state of turmoil, to provide an excuse to interfere and dominate the area, and serve their own purposes any time they wished.

Since its inception, Ismailia has experienced repeated war and devastation: during the German air raids on allied troops in WWII, the 1948 War with Israel, the Suez War with England, France, and Israel in 1956, the Six Days War with Israel in 1967, the War of Attrition 1967-1973, the Egyptian Crossing of the Canal in 1973.

I used to think with utter frustration about the politicians and religious fanatics: why could they not rise above the dogmatic differences and extend their limited vision? Why could they not think of the others as human beings: as fathers, mothers, sisters, brothers, or children? Why could they not comprehend the underhanded designs of the super powers? Perhaps then they could see the insanity of war and the inhumanity of racism.

We, the children of Ismailia, cared little for the trappings of power. We were too far removed from the grand capitals, where politicians created their empty slogans and ambitious dreams. Nor did religion seem to be an issue, for we had learned too much to be restricted to any one belief. There is only one God, to worship any way one chooses. We clearly understood the problem for what it was. We lived a simple life — for the **sake** of life. The insanity of war and the absurdity of people seeking power shattered our peaceful existence.

But war came... it destroyed our peace, our homes and our people. I can see it still: Noussah the beautiful nurse... Ahmed the delightful child... Ibraheem the distinguished looking man... all lying on the ground, torn to pieces, and swimming in blood. My mind is blown away with the savage explosions. I am shocked and horrified by the scene... it leaves me shaken, lost, bewildered, and sick. I do not know how to cry. My voice fails me. I cannot utter a scream or release my rage. It is not only people who die, but also horses, dogs, cats, trees, and flowers. I am at a loss to adequately explain the true horror, the stench of death, and the raging anger that fills me... I am overwhelmed by feelings of emptiness, helplessness, and the absurdity of it all. As I was to learn, these emotions stay forever. My young friend Youssri stood next to me just a few seconds ago. He was breathing, talking, laughing, and full of youthful ambitions. Suddenly he is blown away, and exists no more. Yet he never carried a gun, nor belonged to a fanatic group or even a political party.

I began to feel irrelevant, and vulnerable. The notion of being blown away any second continued to haunt me — day and night. The shocking truth that life is extremely fragile, and the realization that people could be utterly stupid, outraged, frustrated, and forever saddened me.

It is strange how we react to a calamity and to a threat. Some may run in fear, some discover in themselves courage they never knew. At times, seeing death and devastation, I was frozen, stone-faced, without emotions, and without tears. Then another time I found tears streaming down my face as I watched a mango tree take a direct hit and go up in flames with its branches, leaves, flowers, and fruit. Perhaps it was a symbol for how indiscriminate are the ravages of war.

The bombs provided an equal opportunity for everything to be destroyed. Bombs did not discriminate between homes, hospitals, churches, or mosques. Everything on the front-line becomes a military target. When your home is suddenly destroyed, it takes away with it your childhood. Gone are the secret hiding places, and the birth place of your brothers and sisters. Everything crumbles in a fleeting moment and leaves you feeling beaten, violated and outraged.

For a few years, Ismailia became sandwiched between the Egyptian and Israeli armies. Egyptian fighter planes were frequently shot down by our "friendly" air defenses. Many people died by "friendly fire." I laughed bitterly at the ironic military term "friendly fire." Fire is simply fire, it burns everybody in its way, the friend, the foe, and the bystander.

War is the ultimate of the most primitive acts. It reduces us to a sub-human level below that of beasts. It is in fact a manifestation of our lack of real power and imagination, of our actual limitations and frustrations. Our retarded human civilization seems to exchange aggression within a given society for aggression towards "the enemies" in other societies. Our human "civilization" gives these aggressive acts legal sanction. We have even established some "accepted rules" for war and for killing, and signed them into official treaties. Somehow it translates: If you kill someone within your own society, you are considered a criminal. On the other hand, if you kill a foe across the border, you are hailed as a hero! This is primitive and utterly insane. We will never become truly civilized unless we eradicate all acts of violence and war. If there are some intelligent beings in outer space they must be looking down, either laughing at our retarded vision, or shaking their heads over our stupidity.

War tore apart the social fabric of Ismailia. Its multi-cultured, wonderful people are scattered throughout the world. Very few are left. Families separated, friendships were broken, and love stories came to an abrupt end. Many lost not only loved ones but also their homes, their jobs, their businesses, and their dignity. Some felt that dying was a better fate than coping with all these losses.

In spite of it all, during the lull between battles, Ismailians came to realize how short, beautiful and precious life is, and how insane the situation had become. We laughed harder, stayed up all night long, loved more passionately, and celebrated life any way we could. Finally, in 1970 I had to give up and bid farewell to our small town by the lake, and emigrate to America, but not without a wound in my spirit and an ache deep into my heart.

Some ten years later I was sitting in my living room in Boston, Massachusetts, watching a live telecast from Jerusalem: The Egyptian President Anwar El Sadat was visiting Israel to seek peace. My wounded heart pounded once again as I watched him descend from his aircraft while Israeli soldiers played the Egyptian national anthem. The feelings were overwhelming, and I struggled to hold back my tears. "Finally, they are catching on," I murmured to myself. "Finally there is hope for humanity after all." I became excited, happy, and full of hope at seeing a dream coming true. I felt sad only for not being there and being a part of this event. But the overwhelming feelings of vindication, triumph, and hope were paramount... I even felt guilty for not liking Sadat before.

A few years later, however, and on the same television set in Boston, I watched the Moslem fanatics assassinate Sadat for daring to seek peace. They sprayed bullets into a reviewing stand where he stood erect and brave.

Another decade passed... and the elusive concept of peace advanced, then contracted, then advanced again... in a slow and frustrating pace. The dogma, the hatred and the myopia continued to blind both sides of the Middle-East conflict.

In 1995, from the Israeli side, another soldier of peace emerges, another convert to sanity, daring to defy the Jewish fanatics, and push for peace. On TV, I watch as the Israeli Prime Minister Yitzhak Rabine, the serious, straightforward and logical leader, is assassinated. The killer is an eerie young Jewish zealot. Ironically, his name is "Amir," my young son's name. He smiles to the cameras as he confesses his horrible crime. Rabine's wife Leah, a courageous and outspoken woman, reads an open letter to her slain husband. She vows to continue to urge her nation to seek peace. She points at the ideology of hatred, and to the fanatics, as the real killers of Rabine, and the enemies of peace. As I watch this scene the tears roll down on my face. I am angry, sad and wounded. How long will it take for the fanatics to comprehend? How much blood must be shed?

When I visit Ismailia, I walk as a stranger among alien newcomers. The people I loved have died, disappeared or moved away. My beloved aunt passed away, many of my schoolmates died in the war, my family and friends are scattered around the world. Everything— the gardens, the buildings, the streets—has changed, aged and decayed. Gone are the colorful cultures that once nurtured my mind. Gone are the people I loved. A young man pushes me aside as he passes by me... I politely object... He asks me sarcastically: *"And where do **you** come from!?"*

Journey

MELODY OF TODAY'S SONNET

ATHENS, GREECE 1970

The flight across the blue Mediterranean from Cairo to Athens was lonely, and brief, yet felt like an eternity. Only a short time ago my family and life-long friends, their eyes on the verge of tears, stood at Cairo airport and bid me farewell. They smiled, but their faces were pale, their eyes sad. I felt numb, but managed to say a few meaningless words, and walked around the terminal with a dull pain in my chest. I found it difficult to breathe, but mumbled a few humorous words that fell flat. Strong emotions were caught in my throat. Tears were too proud, or too petrified to flow.

The decision to leave home, country and memories behind, to go far away and start a new life, is agonizing for anyone who does it. For me, leaving home was an admission that hope had run out on me in that land. Still, I found striving to live according to my ideals and rejecting worn-out values to be much more powerful than the agony over severing my roots — even those far reaching and tender roots that threatened to hold me back.

It was time to tear away the layers that suffocate and camouflage one's identity, time to remove the mask of conformity and lassitude.

"Why stop in Greece?" I wondered. I think the choice came to be for several complex reasons, some conscious, some subconscious, and some I still do not quite understand. Were there mysterious magnetic powers attracting me? Were there unexplained spiritual connections luring me? I was always fascinated by Greece.

Perhaps I needed to stop to gasp for air on the opposite side of the Mediterranean, and give my pain a chance to subside a little... Possibly, I needed to see some familiar faces before I plunged into the unknown. Or, maybe subconsciously, I came to Athens looking for answers, or for a guide to light the foggy path before me. This is my first stop on a long journey to a faraway land. All I have is one suitcase and a one-way ticket to a destination half way around the world. I stop and stare at the words listed on my itinerary: Cairo — Athens — Rome — New York — San Francisco. The words look surreal, like a list of exotic cities in some geography lesson. Am I really going to pass through all these places in a few days? Can it be possible? Somehow it doesn't seem real... but here I am, making my first stop: Athens, Greece.

The Greeks tried to answer eternally perplexing questions: What is the best life? What is the ultimate good? What is virtue? How can we find happiness? What is the ideal conduct?... Greek philosophy provided the first substantive thoughts that occupied my mind.

The plane skims swiftly over the warm blue waters of the Mediterranean, descending rapidly as we approach the beautiful and rugged beaches of Greece. We pass over bare brown hills and small white houses that look bleached by the sun. The plane finally lands on the black tarmac with a thud, then taxis towards the large white terminal with a loud, wailing, annoying noise.

I step out of the plane onto the open platform and look around me. Although it is winter, it feels warm, even hot. The sun reflects brightly off the naked hills. The land looks thirsty and lifeless, except for a few olive trees in the far distance, and white homes scattered randomly among the hills. As I walk down the portable steps, the smell of jet fumes mingles with the salty sea breeze and makes me a bit dizzy.

Anxious feelings overtake me as I walk towards the terminal. I think to myself: What will I do on the shores of the Pacific? How will I get along? Will I meet some success, or utter failure?... I have no specific answers, no detailed plans, no assurances, and no one even to talk to. I have nothing but hope, hunger, and a few vague dreams. I am driven by a sharp pain in my heart, by revolt against narrow- mindedness, and by a yearning for personal freedom. Although I want to be free to express myself without suffering the wrath of a restrictive society, I feel the pain of leaving my family and friends. At the same time I am angered by the absurdity of the Middle East. My hopes and dreams of a better life are mixed with apprehensions of the unknown. I gaze at the bare hills, the small white houses and the olive trees. Somehow I am able to transform my emotions into a propelling power to act, to move on, to go far away to another land.

My Greek friends are supposed to meet me here at the airport. I am yearning to see their faces. Again, I feel the anguish and the lump in my throat. War in the Suez separated us a few years earlier. I feel sad at the thought that I might never see them again. I walk around the terminal, among the crowds of passengers, with a heavy heart. Suddenly, I hear someone calling my name, and see one of my friends running to greet me. Emotions overwhelm me and I become speechless. It is good to see a familiar face full of smiles and washed with tears.

We drive to downtown Athens in a small car. The radio is on, and I listen to old, familiar Greek music. It warms my wounded heart. It brings back memories of many good times, of the dancing parties on the roof of the Greek Club in Ismailia. We pass by the Acropolis. "Am I really here?" I whisper to myself.

At a cafe near Parliament Square we sit, reminiscing about Ismailia — the small town by the lake that we all left behind. We trade jokes and war stories, tease each other a bit, and consume a few bottles of Ouzo. I can't help but like the Greek people... I admire not only the ancient, profound wisdom they contribute to humanity, but also their genuine and sincere warmth, their absolute passion for music, for dance, and for life.

I dig deep into my memories and search for the lessons I have learned from the Greeks. One thought stands out from Aristotle, who articulated the ideal conduct: *"Extremes are vices, and the middle qualities are virtues. Between cowardice and rashness lies courage, between humility and pride lies modesty, and between gloominess and buffoonery lies good humor."*[1] Aristotle advocated the "Golden Mean," i.e. to follow the middle of the road and the best fit between extremes. I have made a vow to myself never to allow anything or anyone to force me to any extreme. Looking back at the extremism that flooded, and still floods, the Middle-East, I realize why I can no longer belong to that culture. I also became keenly aware of the way I strive to be, and the ideal conduct I must pursue. Aristotle proposed another significant thought: *"The ultimate virtue is neither power nor love, it is rather intelligence."*[2] With intelligence one can find the proper balance and the virtuous way between extremes and vices. I vow to become neither an oppressive power-seeker nor a submissive follower. I believe virtue lies in intelligent, balanced, free choice.

In his book on Ethics, Aristotle describes the ideal man:

> *"He does not expose himself to danger since there are few things for which he cares sufficiently; but he is willing in great crisis to give even his life, knowing that under certain conditions it is not worth living... He is open in his dislikes and preferences; he talks and acts frankly... He is never fired with admiration since there is nothing great in his eyes... He never harbors malice and always forgets and passes over injuries... He bears the accidents of life with dignity and grace, making the best of his circumstances... He is his own best friend and takes delight in privacy."*[3] — These are words I want to live by.

My Greek friends took me out dancing — on a clear, warm and enchanting night — to a Cafe in Akharnon, a suburb of Athens, and full of fun-loving people. The music is passionate, the rhythm sensual, and everybody is in a festive and joyous mood. We laugh until it hurts, drink and eat like there is no tomorrow. We smash dishes on the floor, to celebrate life, to release tension, and to keep with the tradition of Greek sailors.

The musicians take a short break. I go outside to cool off and stand in the dark of the night, under a clear sky full of stars. I remember when I was a young boy, a Greek friend took me to see a film called *Zorba the Greek*. Zorba was the creation of the great Greek writer Kazantazakis. Zorba was a man who loved life and celebrated it in every passing moment. He never allowed the absurdity of life to keep him down, nor dampen his lively spirit. He enjoyed his life, moment to moment, and tried, with good humor, to make the best of everything. He cherished life even though he could not fully understand its limitations or disappointments. He didn't look back to the past with nostalgia, or forward to the future with fantasy. He dealt with the present, with what was real and concrete.

> *"Zorba: That's how I am. There's a devil in me who shouts, and I do what he says. Whenever I feel choking with some emotion, he says 'Dance!' and I dance. And I feel better."* [4]

Kazantazakis crafted Zorba to be a complex character, and varied in dimensions. Zorba was careless, frivolous, and fun-loving but at the same time capable of being a profound thinker. His inquisitive and intuitive mind was always engaged — searching, probing and challenging:

Zorba: *"It's a mystery (he murmured) a great mystery! So, if we want liberty in this bad world, we've got to have all those murders, all those lousy tricks, have we?... How does a plant sprout and grow into flower on muck and manure?"*

Scholar: *"Say to yourself Zorba, that the muck and manure is man and the flower is liberty."*

Zorba: (Striking his fist on the table) *"But the seed? For a plant to sprout there must be a seed. Who put such a seed in our entrails? And why doesn't this seed produce flowers from kindness and honesty? why must it have blood and filth?"* [5]

Zorba left a profound impression on me. To a great degree, his character impacted my attitude towards life and the way I was able to deal with its capricious nature. For years, however, the degree of such an influence was obscure, I only realized its full extent when I reached adulthood. Zorba's magical way of coping with adversities and absurdities helped me. He modeled the way as he dealt with losses and disappointments, and as he faced a world of paradoxes, and perplexities. He showed me how to open all my senses to see, hear, touch, taste, and feel the world as if for the first time. He taught me to approach life as if I should never die, and cherish everything in life as if I am going to die at any moment.

The band plays another festive tone. I take another sip of Ouzo and search for a pen. I borrow one from the waiter, and write on a paper napkin :

I love life and seize every moment
never allow the insane fray
to spoil the melody of today's sonnet
nor shatter the peace in my heart.
I live in the real, the concrete,
never a hostage to a nostalgic past.
I deal with what is here, right now
not with a fantasy of what is to come.

An early light of dawn intrudes through the glass windows of the cafe, without apology. It is time to say goodbye to my dear friends, time to get back to the airport to continue my journey aboard the silver bird. While the city still sleeps, my flight takes off and I look down from my window on the city of Athens and the Greek shoreline. There is a faint smile on my face for the sweet memories, and a dull ache in my heart for all the pain, but with a determination to go on, come what may!

Life

Paris was rainy, windy and desolate. Alone, I walked with my hands in the pockets of my raincoat. Cold rain dripped on my face like large tear drops. Passing by the almost empty cafes on Montparnasse Avenue, I felt cold, exhausted, and somewhat sad for no apparent reason. My shoes were soon soaking wet, and I began to shiver from the damp and the cold wind. Cars were scurrying along the avenue, sweeping through large pools of water, splashing like fountains in every direction. They scampered as if desperately fleeing the miserable weather.

Although I felt lonely and cold, somehow I also felt in touch with my own feelings. They mirrored the gloomy scene on Montparnasse on that rainy day. The initial excitement and glamor of international business travel had worn out after the first few years. Later on, international trips became nothing but agony: all airports start to look the same, all foods become tasteless, the jet lags seem to persist, even become a permanent condition ... the indifferent and empty faces I meet seem to appear and reappear... the luggage claims... the Customs check points... the flight delays... the enterprising taxi drivers... the plastic picture frames in the look-alike hotel rooms... the tourist traps.

Is this the price I must pay?

After having several brushes with death in Egypt during the war, emigration to America, the struggle and hard work to pursue a career, graduate school, marriage, children, and then divorce ... life had left me with an empty feeling, and a bitter taste in my mouth.

I decided to seek shelter in one of the small cafes on the avenue to warm my tired body and hide from the rain. I sat at a small table in the corner of the cafe near a large glass window that looked out on a major intersection. The waiter gave me a sympathetic look and brought me a cup of hot, steaming coffee. I took off my wet shoes and began to feel somewhat warmed, and became pensive.

Now, Paris creates within me two distinctive and contradicting feelings: on the one hand, I am charmed and entertained by its structural beauty, elegance and vividness. On the other hand, the city makes me feel cold, alienated and even melancholy. Paris is perhaps the worst place on earth to find yourself alone and feeling lonely on a dismal, wet afternoon.

The rain slowly let up and the sky revealed a hint of blue here and there. Men and women of all colors and shapes started to fill the sidewalks and the cafe. Gradually, the sounds of rain falling and cars splashing were displaced with the hum of Parisians chit-chatting, dishes clattering and waiters shouting their orders. The abhorrent cigarette smoke started to form a bluish-gray cloud hovering over my table. It mingled with the strong smell of the French coffee and gave me a headache. I withdrew from the smoke and the noise to the comfort of my inner thoughts. What am I doing here in Paris in this cafe? Why am I traveling almost nonstop and finding myself lonely wherever I land ? Why am I spending most of my time hanging between the earth and the clouds. Why am I jumping from country to country and sitting in small cafes amongst strangers?

The cafe was teeming with all varieties of humanity: the ordinary,

the extra-ordinary, and the bizarre. I noticed each person had a different
expression on his or her face; each seemed to have a unique preoccupation.
The faces around me reminded me that each of us is on a mysterious
journey and does not know exactly where it will lead. Each of us is
distracted by some temporary illusion, some capricious game, some
transient surge of joy or jolt of pain. Each lives, struggles, grows old…
sometimes finds happiness and sometimes finds sadness. At the end, will
we all die without knowing exactly why we lived?… I questioned my
purpose, my being, my solitary existence…

I remember reading Soren Kierkegaard, the Danish Existentialist,
who expressed similar feelings: *"I stick my fingers into existence, it smells
of nothing. Where am I? What is this thing called the world? Who is it
who has lured me into this thing… and now leaves me here? Who am I?
How did I come into the world? Why was I not consulted?"*[6]

I echo Kierkegaard's thoughts and add my own protest: *"This life
will end one day… I will die without anyone asking my opinion. What
kind of joke is this?"*

Kierkegaard also expressed the frustration many feel about the
inability to understand it all: *"We understand life backward, but we only
can live it forward."*[7] For me, there is no simpler nor more accurate
statement than this, to describe how limited we are. We walk through life
almost blindfolded. We are doomed to repeat the mistakes everyone made
before us. We are naive, myopic, and busy pursuing our silly ambitions.
We are often confused by what others expect of us, or find ourselves
entangled in meaningless games. Meanwhile life is rushing by — the fine
sand is slipping through the hour-glass.

When we finally start to comprehend something about life, when
we start to come closer to the truth, time suddenly becomes our enemy.
We find ourselves at the end of the road with no way to get back to
the beginning.

As a child I was fascinated with Omar Khayyam's poem about the riddle of life. I first read it after losing my younger sister, Rofeyya, who died from a simple fever when she was only four years old.

> *"In and out, above about below,*
> *Tis nothing but a magic shadow-show,*
> *Played in a box whose candle is the sun,*
> *Round which we phantom figures come and go."* [8]

Life is nothing but a shadow-show — an ethereal and illusive experience? We are here it seems for a few fleeting moments. We dance through life like phantom figures, distracted temporarily by a clever show, orchestrated by an unseen magician we call God.

We cannot make up our minds whether to laugh or cry over life. Some see life as a comedy, others see it as a painful tragedy. Racine, the 18th century French writer, tried to reconcile those two views of life when he wrote: *"Life is a tragedy for those who feel and a comedy for those who think."* [9] Perhaps I may add: *life is a tragic-comedy for those of us who are condemned to have both sensitive feelings and inquisitive minds.*

Do those with higher intellectual capacity and a greater sense of humor see life as a joke, a game and a shadow-show?

Can they laugh at life's absurdities and enjoy the positive aspects, while making light of its negative and painful aspects? Although I have tried to become one of these people, I have not always been successful. I find it sometimes not easy to laugh when the pain is so overwhelming.

On the other hand, those who have deep feelings and higher sensitivity to the human pain and suffering, often see life as a tragedy: a constant struggle, an endurance and a painful existence; a time for bleeding wounds and tearful hearts. Admittedly, at times I have felt this way, especially during my experience with war in Egypt, and when

I lost my father. Those painful memories are hard to overcome or to brush aside.

Nevertheless, even in the darkest of hours, life has ways of putting a smile on our miserable faces. I like what Marcus Aurelius the Roman emperor-philosopher wrote: *"I am happy despite what happens to me... Why? Because I continue to be."*[10] I think what he meant is that the simple act of being alive must be enough to make us happy and joyful. There is no other purpose for life than life itself... Nothing is a more meaningful or more noble reason than that. We come to life to make our dreams come true, to create our own purpose and then achieve it before we die. We can accept the pain and celebrate the joy of life while it lasts.

The writings of the French-Algerian writer Albert Camus also, for many reasons, captured my imagination. Perhaps because he loved life in spite of its imperfection and absurdity; or because he had a passion for the sea; or maybe because he was a product of the French, Arab, and Greek cultures of the Mediterranean where I grew up. Camus wrote: *"The world is absurd and life is too short. What is really absurd is our need to understand life while life is incomprehensible to our still limited minds. Life eludes us because it cannot be reduced to any simple human meaning."*[11]

Maybe we are trying too hard to make life understandable and subject to the analysis of our limited logic. We become frustrated and confused because we cannot force life to fit our simple explanations. Although life is difficult to understand and often ridiculous, this does not make it meaningless. Life is also beautiful, enjoyable and precious. Even a man or a woman near death clings to dear life, for life itself — for another breath, for another day of living. At that point he or she must have found a great value and a profound need for life.

I believe we must revolt against death and anything that makes death meaningful. We must accept life, even if it is difficult to understand, even if sometimes it disappoints us. We must go on enjoying the act of living while defying death at all times.

Abraham Maslow, the American writer, after experiencing a heart attack wrote:" *The fragility of life makes it doubly precious. Like a delicate flower, the secret of its beauty is in the brevity of its life and the frailty of its existence.*"[12]

So, I ask myself again, "What does this all mean? Have I now arrived at the true meaning of life?" No, the reality of life is still a mystery and a riddle; no human mind can shed enough light to explain it. But even if it is incomprehensible, life is precious, painful, joyful, and wonderfully absurd.

The waiter stopped at my table with another hot cup of coffee, interrupting my thoughts and my internal wondering. I thanked him and took a few sips, and returned to my day-dreaming and my wondering. I began to write my thoughts:

Of course, I came to life without being consulted

It is certain, I will die without having a choice

For sure, this has to be a tragic comedy

No one can understand life completely

I can understand some of it backward

But I can only live my life forward

There is no time for me to waste

It is slipping away in utmost haste

I must accept life as a capricious game

Everything has to end, nothing is forever

But I will not take this lying down

I will fight death, and continue to endeavor

I must be free to choose

To define who am I and what am I

My real self is an unfinished painting

It will never be complete until I die

WIND PASSION

Passion

MARTINIQUE 1984

Our plane shakes violently in sudden moves as we pass through strange-looking cloud formations. They look more like a field of huge mushrooms, or smoky results of hundreds of nuclear explosions...
It feels like I am on a roller-coaster and every now and then thrown off track. My stomach does not seem to appreciate such wild gymnastics, but I counsel myself: this must be the nature of the tropical weather.

The bouncy ride does not seem to bother other passengers as much. They drank too much during the flight to be concerned with what happens around them. They are an interesting collection of people of every color, shape, age, and background: a hairdresser from New Jersey and his curly-haired girlfriend, a Canadian couple on their honeymoon, a police officer with a sense of humor from Marina del Rey, a group of French students, three loud, young women from Texas. The only thing they all seem to have in common is a determination to enjoy themselves.

This is my first vacation-trip to the Caribbean... I wanted to escape the snow and the wind-chill factor of Boston, the drudgery and the wild swings of high technology business, the pain and agony of my divorce, and find solace on the beaches of Martinique.

Finally the plane breaks through the mushroom clouds and the mist reveals the gorgeous and enchanting island. Dark-green vegetation covers the hills, white sand outlines its beaches and lagoons, and clear teal-blue water hugs its shores. Somehow, the plane lands safely on a small strip of a somewhat-paved runway.

A warm, humid wind greets my face and blows my hair wildly in every direction as I descend to the ground. The moist air engulfs me in a clammy embrace as I walk towards the modest and dark wooden building serving as a terminal. The small interior is hot and humid with no air-conditioning. I begin to feel tired, irritated, and impatient to move on. The bureaucratic ceremonies — the lines, the passports, the stamps, the luggage-check, seem to go on for an eternity. I feel over-anxious to reach the beach, to relax, and release a sigh of relief.

At the bus station, we line up to ride an old beaten-up yellow bus with no glass in its windows. The yellow color is fading, brown-orange rusty spots are gaining ground and seem to obliterate whatever is left of the original yellow. The air becomes more oppressive and makes breathing somewhat difficult. The other passengers become silent and signs of fatigue spread over their features.

Our Caribbean driver is an enchanting man. He speaks English with a heavy French-Caribbean accent and exhibits a great sense of humor. His skin is dark as a night without a moon, but when he smiles his white teeth sparkle, and no one can help but smile back. He drives the beaten-up yellow bus like a race-car driver competing in the Grand Prix.

The narrow road to our resort village twists, curves, climbs, and descends the hills that hug the shore line. Every now and then a glimpse of a beautiful beach appears, then disappears behind tropical trees. On the bus my fellow passengers remain quiet. We are hot, tired, jet-lagged, and anxious to reach the village, but the ride seems endless. The wheels and axles of the poor old bus squeak and moan as if in protest at the driver's abuse.

A crowd of sun-tanned, friendly and joyous people wearing bathing suits, and with seashells around their necks, are waiting for us at the

Buccaneers Village. Music is blasting with an irresistible beat. It is a French-Caribbean song, "C'est bon pour la morale." The catchy tune, the alluring beat, and the warm welcome ignites a positive mood for the tired and the weary until finally, a contagious smile is on every face.

From that point on, and for a short and precious week I became relaxed, and found a peaceful side of myself. I spent my days running on the beach at dawn until the sun came out of hiding behind the hills; sunbathing on the soft and warm white sand; diving in the inviting blue waters of Buccaneers Bay, and feasting on tropical fruits and exquisite French food.

Most significantly, I became instantaneously addicted to something both healthy and exhilarating: I learned to windsurf. My teacher was a young, French, demanding, precise, patient, and very expressive woman. She was small, loud, and had the manner of a commanding naval officer...

Slowly I learned how to find my "sea legs" — that is, to balance myself on the wobbly board floating on the waves, to lift my sail from the water, and to counter-balance my weight against the force of the wind. Slowly I learned to choose my direction while finding an equilibrium between the forces of the wind, the friction of the sailboard, and the weight of my body. I learned to exploit the wind, sail with accelerating speed, change course, and let the wind help me do it.

Soon I found myself windsurfing alone on the blue-green waters of Buccaneers Bay... I felt liberated, as free as a bird, exhilarated as I raced with the wind. I glided over the waves with my small sailboard carrying me around as if in a dream... I felt the heat of the tropical sun turning my skin color to bronze... I felt the wind blowing through my hair... I listened to the relaxing sound of my board as it skimmed over the waves. I tried to keep my consciousness focused on the moment, for fear of missing even a drop of this magical play.

The love of windsurfing inundated me like a sudden fever. It continues to flame and to grow stronger over the years. The feelings that it creates in me are beyond simple description: to be one with wind, sea and sky, and to be alone. To be propelled by the force of wind is a feast for the soul. I feel confirmed, blessed and free... The joys and playfulness of a child are once again mine, basking and enjoying the best life can offer. Nothing is more significant than having the sun, the wind and the sea to play with... The sun bakes my skin and the water sprays my face and cools my body, the wind caresses my hair.

Windsurf...
You carry me away
from everything
and everyone...
Like water I come,
like wind I go
beyond contamination,
babble, and where
no annoyance exists...
Nothing distracts me from
the beauty, serenity,
and significance of the sea.
Only the wind,
the waves, the sky and I.

You magnify my aloneness
my self-reliance...
I strike an equilibrium
between me and nature...
I exploit the wind
to carry me on the waves
to where I will to be...

One early morning I woke up feeling happy. I opened the door of my bungalow, and stood gazing at the breath-taking scene. The turquoise green bay was calm and glistening in the warm morning sun, reflecting the blue of the sky. Its surface was as clear as a mirror except where a soft breeze wrinkled its face here and there, and added touches of a darker hue. Tropical trees embraced and protected the still sleeping village. Small, brightly painted boats were scattered about the bay like wild flowers. The scene was waiting to be discovered by a painter with a passion for beautiful landscapes.

I took a deep breath, lowered my shoulders and felt peaceful for a change. My heart was full once again. Two white seagulls were performing their dazzling morning dance, soaring high in the sky then gliding low in harmony with speed and grace. They made me smile. I felt a strong urge to take a long walk on the sandy beach.

I fell in love with Martinique. It is the perfect place to celebrate the passion for life. The people here are always in a happy mood. It must be the impact of constant sun, gentle wind, beautiful beach, and life of leisure.

I walked on the beach, listening to the sounds of the gentle waves caressing the sand. The faint cries of seagulls were soothing. The soft breeze upon my face made me relax.

At last I had managed to escape the turmoil, the ties, and the disappointments. Now I could think about the new life I should lead.

The sunshine grew brighter, the breeze felt warmer as I walked down closer to the water's edge. I took my shirt off and lay down on the yellow, soft, inviting sand, letting the tropical sun warm my soul and bake my skin. Gradually, the breeze turned into stronger gusts and the waves rushed to shore with greater force.

At the edge of the horizon a tall ship moved slowly across the blue sky with its snowy white sails billowing in the wind. The ship keeled elegantly windward and created a bubbling foam in front of its bow. To me, there is always something romantic and thrilling about a tall ship; it has excited my imagination since I was a child. I remembered reading *The Journeys of Sinbad* and *The Trips of Marco Polo*. They both fascinated me and kindled a passion within me for travel and adventure.

For some unexplained reason, I found the words of the Arab-American poet Khalil Gibran echoing through my consciousness: *"Your reason and your passion are the rudder and the sails of your seafaring soul. If either be broken, you can but toss and drift, or else be held at a standstill in mid-sea."* [13]

I smiled quietly to myself. Admittedly, I have struggled, all my life, to balance flames of passion with calmness and calculation of reason. Intellectually, I always knew that if I allowed my passion to flame uncontrolled, it might turn into a raging fire that could consume me and everything around me. On the other hand, if I allow reason alone to rule my life, it could become a confining force that binds me in a lifeless mold.

In spite of this clear understanding, I have found myself frequently erring on one side or the other. I always yearned to perfect the art of fine-tuning, to strike an equilibrium between these two extremes. I discovered that one cannot simply do away with one or the other. Spinoza, the 15th century Jewish philosopher, reaffirmed this paradox when he wrote: *"If passion without reason is blind — reason without passion is dead!"* [14]

So what is the secret to finding an equilibrium between the winds of passion and the light of reason? What keeps that windsurfing board balanced, gliding swiftly over the waves, and heading to the desired direction? How is it done with such grace and such force?

Passion is the vital force. It is the force and the flame that motivate all of us to act. It is the sail and the wind that carry the sailboard forward. Without it, life would be tasteless, colorless and motionless. Certainly, we must be analytical and calculating when charting a course, before embarking on a journey. But no one is going anywhere without the passion to act and the energy to propel himself into motion.

Knowing that life is finite, gives me more reason to live passionately and to play each role in life with tremendous intensity. It makes me pour my heart into everything I do.

Reason, on the other hand, is the guiding light, the navigational compass and the rudder that keeps our ship on course. It is the calculation we make before embarking on a journey. Without reason we lose our way; we only drift aimlessly on tumultuous and confusing seas.

In the end, it is the seasoned sailor who is capable of making it all work together to serve his purpose. Unfortunately, experience and mastery do not occur over night, and not without pain. Mastery is a fine art, attainable only after years of trials, errors and heart aches. That day in Martinique I made a vow to continue to seek this balance, for it is only the tenacious and persistent sailor who can hope to achieve it.

I did not know how long I lay watching the ship, but I felt the sun burning my skin. I put my shirt on and climbed back to the street. I was hungry all of a sudden. On the street facing the sea I found a small restaurant with outside tables. The white table cloth was crowned with fresh red blossoms in a crystal vase. The vase reflected the rays of the sun and splashed colors of the rainbow on the table cloth. I sat closest to the street, ordered a bottle of white wine, a dish of "Fruits de Mer" and a loaf of exquisite French bread, and had myself a feast. It was a simple joy to relax, soak up the sun, and savor the wine.

I picked up a pen and wrote:

Sail the ship of your soul,

as a seasoned sailor of the high seas

who knows how to exploit the wind

and not drift aimlessly in the breeze

Chart your course in light of reason,

sail away with winds of passion

that lead to destinations

only audacious dreams can fashion

Truth

CAMBRIDGE, MASSACHUSETTS   1986

The storm comes to an end, and the roads are now partially clear of snow and ice. Snow paints everything with cotton-white: trees, rooftops, sidewalks, even people's hair. The air is cold, crisp and piercing. A white carpet reflects the street lights, the colorful Christmas lights, cars' headlights, and compels darkness to vanish.

Despite freezing temperatures, icy roads, and New Englanders' casual disregard for driving rules, a festive and a tolerant mood inhabits Cambridge, a town across the Charles river from Boston. Christmas is approaching and people are swarming in and out of the buildings and shops surrounding Harvard square, carrying bundles of gift-wrapped packages of all colors and shapes.

Christmas in New England has a unique character and charm. Old colonial buildings of dark-red bricks contrast appealingly with the snow-covered, triangular-shaped roofs. Lights of every color of the rainbow adorn buildings, trees and telephone poles. The smell of burning logs mingles with the smell of fresh baked cookies, and smoke billows flare out the old chimneys. Holiday music comes from every direction. The town is certainly in a festive, excited holiday mood.

I walk briskly across the park near Harvard University's old campus, en route to Cafe Au Bon Pain for some hot coffee. My heavy coat, scarf, gloves, and long boots fail to keep me warm. The penetrating cold wind sends shivers through my entire body. I start to run to keep my blood circulating, and get warm.

A crowd is gathered in the entrance of an old building. I approach and mingle in. They are listening to classical music played by four talented young musicians seated on antique wicker chairs. There are two women and two men in the quartet: one woman is shapely with wild, curly red hair; the other is small, fragile, with fine features and a face full of freckles; one bearded young man has thick glasses resting on a distinguished large nose; the other is small framed, with a round red face and blond hair.

The four look like devoted students of music who love to perform any chance they can, regardless of the circumstances. Their cheeks are beet-red, and their fingers almost blue from the cold. Their heads and bodies are swaying with the rhythm, totally absorbed in the divine music they are making. Their eyes are focused on their notes which flap in the brisk wind that rattles the black-metal music stands. They play Vivaldi's Four Seasons flawlessly. The music makes me forget the snow and the shivering cold. I proceed across the square with a feeling of enchantment, mulling over the reasons for my presence on campus.

I enrolled in a graduate program at Harvard University Extension, one designed for people like me — who work for a living. All classes took place in the evenings to allow for a full working day. I enjoyed the classes for the intellectual stimulation and for the enriching exchange of views and life-experiences they fostered. My fellow students were mostly people in their thirties and forties, middle and high-level managers who possessed, on an average, one other graduate degree. They came from varying industries, and from a mix of cultural backgrounds, world-wide.

The study groups, the lively debates, and the endless humor created a healthy distraction from the constant pressures of the business world, and from the painful feelings of separation from my children. I certainly needed some distraction. I was also delighted that the company I worked for agreed to pay the cost of a second graduate degree in Business.

Finally, I make it to the cafe across the square. I need a hot cup of coffee, and some time to read the required chapters. I also want to attempt to de-mystify an assigned case study. I sit near the warm air vents and open my notes, frantically trying to speed-read the lengthy material and hoping for a stroke of brilliance or divine chance to decipher the case.

The cafe is noisy, distracting, and filled with undergraduate students mixed with bizarre-looking people in a strange mishmash of attires. Some have purple hair and dark-blue painted lips. Some have pierced every possible part of their faces with all types of rings. They look like members of some primitive tribe! Since they do not seem to mind my business suit, however, I feel I have no right to mind their ways.

I remind myself that there is no time for idle observation, and return to my reading. Eventually, I take a last sip of coffee and a bite of French pastry, gather my notes and hurry to the lecture hall. The freezing temperature hits me in the face once more, as I make my way by the library. The old campus certainly has a vintage dignity, and the white snow adds a romantic touch to its classic look.

My fellow students are in fine shape tonight. The debates are livelier than ever, the arguments and counter-arguments are long, and sprinkled with colorful dashes of humor. The more we debate the more it becomes clear: despite all valiant attempts to make "Business Management" a science, the human factors and social dynamics impel it to remain, for the most part, an art form.

The three hours pass with lightning speed. Since I am not eager to face the cold weather again, I am the last person to leave the class. After a full day of work, the long commute to Cambridge in the snow, and the three hour class, my brain is on overload. My body is absolutely numb from tiredness and I start to question my own sanity:

Why am I doing this to myself?
Why am I here, still learning at this stage of my life?

What purpose does this serve?

I walk across the campus past the library and the old lecture halls, feeling excessively tired, overworked, lonely, and baffled. In the dim light, hidden behind the bare branches of trees, I notice a sign carved in stone on the face of a building. It contains only one simple Latin word "Veritas"— Truth. I have seen this sign hundreds of times before: all over the buildings, even splashed on cheap insignia and notebooks. It never had any special meaning for me, but for some reason, tonight, this old familiar and timeworn sign strikes me deep in my core, a sudden symbol of what I am looking for. Suddenly it relates to my unquenchable desire to search and discover the Truths…

Yet, after a lifetime of search, there are no final conclusions, no definitive answers, no clear cut explanations. After centuries of study and analysis, all we humans have are theories and probabilities. The more we discover, the more we realize how much we do not know. All the absolutes of science come tumbling down with new discoveries and new ways of looking at things. Everything is in a state of flux, everything is relative: time, space and even mass. The Uncertainty Principle clouds any concrete conclusions in physics. Science remains impotent in the face of AIDS, cancer, or even the common cold.

Richard Feynman, the celebrated American physicist, admitted:

> *"We do not yet know all the basic laws (of nature): there is an expanding frontier of ignorance… Each piece, or part, of nature is always merely an approximation to the complete truth, or the complete truth as far as we know it. In fact, everything we know is only some kind of approximation… Therefore, things must be learned only to be unlearned again or, more likely, to be corrected."* [15]

The work of Stephen Hawking in cosmology is a perfect example of this point: First he proved mathematically that the universe had to start as a "Singularity," before the "Big Bang." Then later, his "No-Boundary" proposal showed us how there might be no singularity after all. One time he asserted that black holes could never get smaller; later he discovered they could.

A poem written by Omar Khayyam centuries ago, unfortunately still holds true — even today:

"To the rolling heaven itself I cried

asking what lamp had destiny to guide

her little children stumbling in the dark?

A blind understanding, heaven replied."[16]

Still, does this mean I should give up the search?

Does this mean I should not challenge my brain? Should I stop searching for the truth? or surrender to despair?

NO.

The intelligent mind must be constantly engaged, never attempting to oversimplify and paint pictures with a wide brush. I must not become content with only one explanation, and only one point of view. That would be shallow — the thinking of an inferior intellect. The fact that truth is not always comprehensible does not mean it does not exist.

The universe is dynamic and changes dimension. Truth is not simply black or white; it is rather a multitude of kaleidoscopic colors. Things vary, circumstances change and the universe continues to expand. Even our own selves: we are not static, predictable, or even consistent beings. We alternate moods, and points of view; we grow, we change. I cannot capture "me" at one moment and put myself in a rigid frame, then call it a true picture. This would be simplistic and expedient, at best. Eventually, one day I will finally reach the end of all my dimensions, when I end this odyssey and exist no more. Then, others may discover who I really was.

Night & Day

SONG TO SAND DUNES

MAUI, HAWAII 1989

An invigorating sea wind blows through my hair, and golden rays of the setting sun bake my skin. Warm sand pebbles stick to my bare feet as I walk along the beautiful beach near Napili. A spectacular Hawaiian sunset is about to take place, and I feel wonderfully awake and aware of its magic... I need to hold on to this precious moment as long as I can.

I walk briskly on the wet sand. Gentle waves dash, splash, and wash my feet. In the middle of the bay I see two huge whales suddenly appear, blowing water into the air like gigantic fountains. I can hardly believe that I am alone on this beach, a solitary human secluded with whales and a golden bay. I wanted every part of my being to become a piece of this wondrous reality.

I had stopped in Maui on my way back to the U.S. from Japan for a short reprieve after a taxing business trip. My heart was in a state of debacle. I was tormented by confusion over what should be primary and what should be secondary in my life: whether it is more important to be true to my own feelings and my need to change, or more important to live according to what everybody else expects. Am I here in this life to fulfill my dreams, or am I here to meet the expectations of others? How can I reconcile my inner feelings with the outer world? I felt like asking the frolicking whales out in the deep, blue-green water to help me find the answers.

For the first time that I can remember, I felt a sudden need to open up and become in harmony with the outside world — a need to step away from my limiting body and liberate myself from haunting thoughts of the past — a need to let my soul run naked along this tropical beach. For a precious few moments, I am out of my introspective self-analysis, able to escape the preoccupations of a soul-searching man.

According to people who claim to know me well, I am "an introverted, sensitive man who possesses a streak of intuition; a contradiction of a thinking person who sometimes can become restless and emotional. A man who always wants all options open." I do not know if I totally agree or disagree with these allegations, but I have to admit that some of them indeed trouble me.

I allow myself to let go of all these haunting thoughts and simply enjoy what surrounds me — the warm wet sand that clings to my toes and to the soles of my bare feet, the soft breeze that engulfs me, and the smell of the sea that intoxicates me. At this point, the obsessive memories of the past do not seem to matter, and fantasies of the uncertain future become irrelevant. All I have is this precious moment on this golden beach. I want to keep it, breathe it, and live it passionately… away from the noise, resorts, and crowds.

Rows of willow trees with long, fluid limbs reach down seductively to touch the foaming waves. I sit on a limb, stretch my legs on the wet, warm sand and watch the reflection of the golden sun on the surface of the water. I finally dare to relax.

Across the bay two small islands are dressed with green hills and volcanic rocks. I see no signs of people nor trappings of civilization. If only I could shift the center of my soul to this beautiful world outside of me… if only I could become the pure energy that belongs to and contains the universe, then I would be in perfect harmony with this world.

Would my paranoid need for security then vanish? Would my craving for sensations then be deemed excessive, and my vanity rendered idiotic? Are these not the true obstacles to peaceful existence? I wonder.

I continue to sit on the curved limb of the willow tree and squint at the water, looking for the two whales. An unexpected feeling of exhilaration runs through me. My heart pounds with joy. I see a few people walking along my remote beach and they look at me and smile broadly, as if recognizing the peaceful feelings within me. "This is amazing," I say to myself. I often provoke a more somber and serious response from strangers. What is different this time? I walk back along the beach and meet more people. I gather more courage to look directly into their eyes and smile broadly. Once again, I receive a smiling response from strangers. I become excited about my simple but significant discovery, and walk on, feeling good about the way these strangers reacted to me. I even look forward to smiling at more of them.

People are like mirrors — they reflect our moods. They are partners in the short journey of life. Show them affinity, and they most often respond in kind. Some can even make our journey more joyful, or at the very least, less painful.

Now, as I near my lodging, the reddish-gold disc of the sun is swallowed into the ocean's far horizon to the west. The sky is painted with every shade of orange, purple and blue. The waves grow higher and rush more eagerly to the welcoming shore. The beach is empty of people once again. The earth has just made its usual turn, and darkness has started to over-shadow the scene. Another day of my life becomes a memory.

It is night now and the sky sparkles with millions of stars. The wind is warm and gentle as I sit on the volcanic cliff overlooking the ocean and the winding beach. Moonlight reflects upon the water's surface. Torches light the narrow path leading to the top of my cliff. Once again,

I am alone. I sip from a glass of red wine that never tasted so sweet. Wind excites the branches of coconut trees behind me, and creates a soothing, hushing sound. I feel at peace.

The whole resort has gone to sleep, the whales have disappeared, the birds have stopped singing. What is wrong with this picture?

Day has turned into night, time is slipping, life is fleeting while everybody languishes. I feel a sudden urgency:

> *Awake !... Awake, I scream within,*
>
> *Stand on your feet*
>
> *Give up the slumber.*
>
> *You only turn into things*
>
> *when you sleep.*
>
> *You become*
>
> *Motionless,*
>
> *Lifeless,*
>
> *Useless,*
>
> *As pieces of stone*
>
> *in a heap.*
>
>
> *Come, hear the waves*
>
> *whispering*
>
> *songs of the universe*
>
> *to the sand dunes.*

Come, bask your soul
in the glow of the moon.
Come, be free as wind can be.
Come, sip the nectar
before the curtains are drawn.

Let no complacency weave
cobwebs in your soul.
Allow no fear to restrict what lies
in your core.
Allow no doubt to blind your vision.
Come, live passionately,
leave behind the fear,
and the indecision.

I take another sip of wine. Passion is now rushing through me like wildfire, my mind teeming, and my heart pounding. I feel alive.

Savor

IBIZA, SPAIN   1990

The song is intense... the music is charged with emotions... the words written by Roe, a young Spanish singer, are blazing, naked, and unflattering. Yet, it draws me in like a butterfly drawn to a burning flame:

"GOTAS DE SANGRE"

TEARS OF BLOOD

"You will cry tears of blood

for a glimpse of freedom

You remain alone, in love, abandoned

Death awaits you in the garden,

along with love, and eternal solitude

You will cry tears of blood

You will meet death

You yearn to walk between the sea and the stars

You want to open your windows to the sunshine

So it may scatter yellow flowers

upon your empty floor..."

At the edge of the rocky cliff where my hotel stands, I lounge and listen to the singer perform. The flaming disc of the sun is about to sink into the calmness of the bay. The charm of this Spanish evening touches my heart. The song is emotional; the music moves me. The singer stands on a small stage, across the swimming pool. His hair is flying wildly in the wind, and his flamenco guitar becomes part of him. His words are depressing, but he sings with an air of defiance, with a decidedly rebellious tone.

Despite the tears, the blood and the loneliness it speaks of, the song kindles a hopeful mood. Its rebellious tone provokes a need to break the shackles, defy death, and search for hope.

I am here in Spain for one week's vacation between two business trips. This is a precious week away from the inhuman race, from the tribulations of the business world, the pressures, the politics, the insanity. This is also my first vacation alone in Europe after a heart-attack, an experience that woke me up to my own limitations. Death awaits me in the garden... time is running out... no way to turn back the clock.

This moment feels like a major transition point. This is a time to assert my love for life and beauty, a time to follow my heart, a time to stop my analytical mind from dominating my actions, time to be the free and passionate child I always wanted to be.

When I finally become able to face the facts of life and death, when I accept that life is totally absurd yet beautiful, when my heart returns to innocence, only then I can be free.

But what is freedom?
Who can tell me?

What does this elusive word mean?

Some people live for it,

others die for it

Nations go to war in its name

Lovers separate to seek it

It has so many dimensions…

Without limitations to challenge, freedom has no meaning. There are basic social boundaries that we accept, in order to co-exist in civility. These insure that our freedom does not infringe on others.

On the other hand, there are limitations that we must never accept: those that violate the core of one's individuality, identity, and reason for being. Any limitation on our individual freedom of self expression, our freedom to choose what we believe, to live according to our own ideals, must never be compromised.

Looking back at the real reasons for leaving my own country, I find that I have fought so hard to win my precious freedom and at a huge cost. For a while, I dreamed of effecting a change in my country, but those were hopeless dreams… The myopic traditions were too entrenched to be eradicated or even modified by a single voice. Mine was a voice in the wilderness… a drop in a sea of myopia and fanaticism.

I quickly recognized the futility of my good intentions and decided it was time for me to depart and seek places where my ideals would be more compatible or, at a minimum, in the prevailing general direction. I promised myself, however, that if my new environment ever became less compatible, I would move on.

I know that being free of what others impose is less fundamental than being free of my own limitations: my own obsessive addiction to overachieving, my own vanity and insecurity. They all threaten my peace of mind, and stand between true happiness and me. Admittedly, I have not yet completely liberated myself from my own self... but I am still trying.

The singer sings another song by Roe. This time the rhythm is so alive, the music more joyful, the words more hopeful:

"SABOREAR"

SAVORING

"You talk to yourself

 about going beyond the horizon

 no longer bound to anything

 seeking life to the ultimate

 You work like a fool

 You laugh at yourself

 You savor this night

 You savor this life"

What good is life, if we do not enjoy it, and savor every moment? This magenta sunset, this enchanting music, this vintage wine, this glorious feeling running through me — I must savor them all. For this moment will never come back.

My hotel overlooks a rugged slope that drops suddenly to an unspoiled, deep and beautiful bay. Strangely this evening, no birds, no ships, no people are in sight. Nothing disturbs the peaceful scene. There are only waves, sky, and a rocky beach.

Night falls peacefully, the wind blows ever so gently. I walk to the edge of the cliff, alone but not feeling lonely. I listen to the waves washing the rocky shore in slow motion, foaming then lashing back in endless succession. Night blankets everything with a cozy shroud. A huge yellow moon rises against the darkened sky, illuminating the scene, taking my breath away. I move slowly, as in a dream, back to my room. I sit on the balcony and watch the moon rising higher and higher… until dawn, I sit, doing nothing, thinking of nothing… only watching the view, listening to the waves, breathing the sea air and… savoring it all.

Courage

IGUACU, BRAZIL 1991

On a short flight from Buenos Aires to the borders of Brazil, the pilot abruptly announces, "We are landing on the Brazilian side, instead of the Argentinean side… we are sorry… the Argentinean airport radar is not functioning… we will try the Brazilian airport."

I release a loud nervous laugh. For some reason, no one else seems to appreciate the humor. I feel somewhat uncomfortable and stare outside the plane's window in silence. Beneath us a densely green carpet of lush vegetation covers every inch of the landscape, as far as the eye can see. For a moment, the horrific thought of crashing in this remote jungle, and never to be found, crosses my mind. The thought lingers in my consciousness, but I quickly force it out.

The plane circles a few times — too close to the tree tops. Suddenly, in the middle of this ocean of green foliage I behold a breathtaking sight. My heart pounds and I press my nose against the window, my eyes wide open with wonder, my mouth agape, and all the rest of my senses filled with wonder and excitement. This is "Las Cataratas," the spectacular waterfalls of the river Iguacu which separates Argentina from Brazil. I want to soak up this spectacular display of nature. I can hardly believe my eyes.

I was unprepared for this. My friends knew about it but chose not to spoil the surprise. I am glad they didn't. Luckily, I have never seen a picture of this wonderful place either. "No picture can match the beauty of this reality," I murmured to myself.

The massive scale of these gorgeous and elaborate waterfalls is amazing. Las Cataratas are multi-directional waterfalls with numerous spectacular points. They cascade in a flowing harmony to three or four plateaus, though there is one sensational focal point. Along the highest drop, the water rushes and merges from three different directions, then falls to the depth of the lower river in a dramatic climax of thunder, foam and mist.

Our plane finally landed on the Brazilian side, and after farcical exchanges with officials we were "released." Although our final destination was indeed Brazil, the bureaucrats insisted that we must return to the Argentinean borders and then re-enter Brazil "legally." It made no difference that we already had valid visas to enter this country.

Bureaucrats everywhere possess an amazing talent for turning paradise into hell with their bizarre rules.

Fortunately, we accepted this situation with a sense of humor— the type of humor one discovers when one experiences an utterly insane episode. All one can do is laugh it off. This is the type of situation that creates instant camaraderie among perfect strangers. Aside from my two French friends, tourists from England, Germany and Argentina formed small informal groups, almost competing for the most hilarious remark. This helped defuse an otherwise tense situation.

The taxi ride to the resort is long. The weather is surprisingly mild for a December day. The forest sparkles with recent rain drops, and smells fresh with hints of fragrance of tropical flowers—like a radiant woman freshly bathed for a night of love. The red soil surrounding the forest is fertile and full of life potentials. It looks ready to burst green, effervescent and bearing fruit.

As we approach our destination, the distant hum of the waterfalls becomes louder and vibrates through the air. It provides a harmonious background to the sharp calls of the tropical birds. Mist rises from the base of the falls into a pale-blue sky, then merges seductively with the scattered white clouds.

The taxi finally arrives at the edge of the waterfall. I step out to the platform overlooking a panoramic view and feel as if I stepped onto the pumping heart of planet earth, whose life-giving water is flowing through veins and arteries of winding rivers and streams. Feeling the vibration in my chest, hearing the passionate rush of water, my heavy heart beats intimately in tune with the powerful cadence. The rhythm embraces me and makes me one with the waterfalls: a life sustaining machine connected to the body of a mortal man, water pulsing through my veins like a torrent.

Water slips through the brooks, streams, and rivers, as easily as time and as quietly as whispers. It may softly bubble and whimper as it gathers momentum along the way. When it arrives at its ultimate fall, its passionate thunder is unleashed.

The falls unshackle the water's mighty energy and magical potential, and everyone takes notice. As the water falls it splashes and sprays while its molecules turn into a misty vapor that rises higher and higher into a waiting sky. Winds swiftly carry the mist to the mountains, turning it to rain and snow, thence flowing through brooks and streams.

Life is utterly absurd
like water, it slips away
to its ultimate fall
At the end of the rainbow
look for no prize
The prize is the journey
you must realize

I lose sense of time, standing with the mist gently glazing my face, and thundering waterfalls shaking my body. For a few moments I stop thinking, and become pure consciousness, aware of everything around me — even myself. I realize more than ever how precious this earth is. I contrast the beauty in front of me with images of the lifeless desolation on planets we have discovered so far. I am grateful to the scientists who produced those images that remind us of how fortunate we are to be human, how lucky to live on our own planet earth.

Hiking around the waterfalls through the lush forests is an exhilarating dream. Beautiful views delight us at every turn, with exotic red, yellow, and violet flowers scattered above and alongside our path. Bright colored tropical birds, large languorous iguanas and other wild animals cross our path at close range, unimpressed by our presence.

I descend slowly to the river's bank, savoring every step of the way. I want to engrave all this magic into my memory forever. At the water's edge, I ride a small motor boat with a few daring souls. We head up river, through some rapids, closer and closer to the base of a focal point of the falls: "The devil's throat," the Brazilian guide declares dramatically. It is a thrilling experience to sit in this small boat at the mercy of a strong current, with gigantic masses of water thundering down above our heads from the top of the falls to the lower river. Our small boat tosses and turns in the tumultuous and foaming water. It is a daring and thrilling ride.

Man finds it rewarding to challenge nature and to test the limits of existence. Perhaps the need stems from a feeling of frustration, of being at the mercy of uncontrollable circumstances — a sort of self-assertion against all inherent limitations.

Every now and then, I need to confront my own limitations and defy all the obstacles which stand in the way of enjoying my life. To some extent, I came to this jungle to confront myself, to find the courage to face reality, accept life's restrictions and cope with my human shortcomings. Subconsciously, I needed to be closer to the vibrating heart of mother earth to deal with this confrontation. I needed this powerful, inundating thunder to overcome the excruciating pain and the babbling noise of inner turmoil.

Later, after midnight, I sit alone with a bottle of wine in the garden near the pool. The air feels humid and warm, the sky is clear, and the stars are sparkling. My mind is occupied with the ideas of courage. I try to write something about courage, and whether I possess any courage at all. I drain the last drop of wine. My brain is assaulted by the loud and eerie noises of insects emanating from the surrounding jungle. The empty wine bottle mirrors my empty soul. I go back to my room to search for another bottle, I find one, bring it back triumphantly and sit at my lonely table. I write these thoughts with the help of Brazilian wine:

> *Do I have the courage to do it all?*
>
> *What is courage?*
>
> *How does it show itself?*
>
> *Should it be something lofty,*
>
> *romantic,*
>
> *dramatic?*
>
> *Could it be simple,*
>
> *ordinary,*
>
> *and happen every day?*

I have recently read a book by a contemporary French writer, Servan-Schreiber, who wrote about courage: "There are only two important kinds of courage: the courage to die, and the courage to get up in the morning." [17] The type of courage he wrote about is not the heroic, dramatic or moralistic courage. It is rather the simple and personal courage needed to face the issues of day-to-day existence. This quiet courage gains no honors, no applause and no audience except oneself.

Courage can only be understood in contrast: it reveals itself when one faces challenges. In the course of my life, I have encountered four basic types of courage:

The courage to face Death,

the courage to face Oneself,

the courage to face Reality,

and the courage to face the World.

Interestingly, these four types of courage form a hierarchy: facing the absurdity of death requires the highest degree of courage. Confronting oneself, with excruciating honesty, is the second most difficult act of courage. Facing the harsh realities of life with grace is the third. Finally, the courage to face the world is the simplest type of courage. It is so, because one can face the world without facing reality, without being honest with oneself, and without facing death.

These four types of courage are independent. That means one can be courageous on one level and an absolute coward on another. This selective form of courage obviously occurs in the best of us. True courage, however, is only proven when one is able to face all four without either extreme fear or extreme rashness.

Facing death, and accepting that life can be lost without logical explanation, demands the pinnacle of courage. If we do not risk feeling pain, courage will have no meaning. Death is the ultimate form of pain. It is the end of life, pleasure, and pursuit of happiness. Courage exists because death is imminent.

It took me decades to be able to face the death of my younger sister, Rofeyya, from a simple fever, when she was only four. It took me longer to accept the death of my father from lung cancer, when he was only forty. For years I refused to accept their sudden and tragic deaths. I buried my anger, horror and rejection. I froze my memories of them. I buried myself in anything that could help me not think about their deaths. I am always struggling, however, with the idea of my own inevitable death. Who dies?... Me?... You must be joking!

I recall Musashi the Japanese Samurai who wrote, *"If you become accustomed to the idea of death, and resolved on death, and consider yourself a dead body... you can pass through life with no possibility of failure."*[18] This is real courage, because it is done in defiance and in spite of being mortal and in spite of facing death.

Facing oneself is perhaps the most complex type of courage. It requires absolute honesty, and a high degree of intelligence, perception and sensitivity. It takes place in the depth of one's soul, in the quiet moments when one chooses to confront his own imperfections and shortcomings. It culminates in an understanding of real self and true worth, and leads to real growth.

Some people may live and die without ever having faced themselves, and perhaps their ignorance is bliss. On the other hand, it is a most tormenting and mind twisting experience, for those who face themselves every day. To them, however, it is a prerequisite of real courage.

Facing reality means facing life's disappointments and absurdities; facing the failures of humanity, in the form of injustice, indifference, and cruelty. It means facing the shortcomings and betrayals of even the people we love. It means accepting the pain and sorrow of reality — accepting them with grace, poise, and a willingness to forgive and forget.

As to facing the world, this takes place when one stands for one's values and acknowledges one's unique identity; when one takes responsibility for one's actions, in spite of the isolation and loneliness it may cause. Honesty, defiance and variance require a great deal of courage: the type of courage that requires me to speak my own mind and tell the truth, though it may clash with social norms, or bring retributions.

At times, I have borne the consequences of daring to speak out and be different. In spite of it all, I have no regrets and offer no apology.

Courage must be an intelligent, optimal and a forward action. It must be acted upon without emotional rashness, without paralysis of fear, and regardless of any imminent danger. The presence of danger gives courage its meaning and its value.

At dawn I drop my pen on the table in exhaustion… I gaze at the two empty wine bottles… I listen to the sounds of the waterfalls in the background… I smile to myself…

I think now I begin to understand.

TRANSIENCY OF SELF

Mind

"So, here it is… Japan… the land of the rising sun," I whispered to myself. Like a feather in the wind, I drifted along and found myself on the other side of midnight. Is this the end of the West or the beginning of the East? Am I really here or is my soul roaming beyond the confines of my body? This is a strange feeling.

I have often felt like a stranger, an outsider — even in Egypt, the country of my birth, and among my own family. I seemed never to conform or to belong to anything or to anywhere in particular. I had no permanent place to call home, no fanatic allegiance to any country, and no flag to die for… I even felt proud of this detached and independent attitude.

Yet the feeling that struck me in Japan was more alienating than ever. I thought, "This country is truly mysterious. It has a language I do not speak, a culture I do not yet understand, and people somewhat difficult to read."

I walked for a while around the crowded streets of Tokyo with a keen awareness, trying to gain a sense of the city. Oceans of people were coming and going in successive waves from every direction. People seemed to be in a hurry, walking fast, with intense expressions on their faces. I seldom saw smiles. Almost all were formally dressed in business clothes: men in their silky, tightly tailored suits, carrying their attaché cases; women in business outfits, walking in groups of three or four. I gazed at strange-looking huge signs with Japanese characters on the store-fronts. They meant nothing to me. They only added to my feelings of alienation.

The plastic displays of menu items in the restaurant windows were a convenient way for me to point at a solitary spaghetti-dish each time I felt hungry. Later I gathered enough courage to venture into tasting some real Japanese dishes. To my surprise I actually liked the unfamiliar food, although most of the time I did not know what I was eating.

With help from some English-speaking people I managed to use the Tokyo subway — a very efficient system. I was struck by the way many passengers were constantly gazing blankly, and making every effort to avoid any possible eye contact. Some were sleeping, some were reading, listening to portable stereos, or simply staring into space.

The Emperor's Palace in downtown looked lonely, as if it belonged to a deep, dark history. It seemed out of place, an anachronism in the midst of a forest of modern sky scrapers, surrounded by a deep canal, and looking like a beleaguered island in the middle of a hostile sea.

This mysterious city intrigued me, and I felt a strong and inexplicable urge to comprehend it, to try to solve its riddle. I felt a need to know the Japanese people: there is something attractive in their traditional ways, something profound in their wisdom, and something graceful in the simple ways they arrange flowers or trim trees.

Although I had only a two-week stay in Tokyo, I felt compelled to try to understand this place. The dramatic time difference kept my body and my mind humming into the early hours of dawn. Sleep seemed to be only an elusive dream.

I sat on the edge of my bed in my hotel room, high above the colorful lights of Tokyo after dark. The city lights flickered, and the whistle of the wind made me feel lonely. I reached for a book on my night table. It was about the teachings of Buddha. I hoped it would give me some clues. I read: *"Make yourself a light. Rely upon yourself. Do not depend upon anyone else."*

Well, I never did. "So what?" I asked.

I read further *"Consider your SELF… think of its transiency. How can you fall into delusions, and cherish pride and selfishness, knowing that they must all end in inevitable suffering. Consider all substances: can you find among them any enduring SELF? Are they not all aggregate and eventually will break apart and be scattered?"* [19]

I paused to think of Buddha's words. I think we tend to forget these simple truths and become entrapped in a meaningless existence. Do we attach value to the valueless? Do these preoccupations distract us to the point where we forget we are only visitors on this planet? Are we that shortsighted?

The wind outside quieted down a bit; some lights were still flickering and others faded away into the dark of the night. I continued my reading: *"The point of the teaching is to control your mind… keep your mind from greed and you will keep your behavior right, your mind pure and your words sincere. By always thinking about the transiency of your life, you will be able to resist greed, anger, and avoid evils. A man's mind may make him Buddha or it may make him beast."* [20]

I smiled and put the book down. I started to feel somewhat peaceful and less troubled. Of course, I thought, controlling one's mind is one of the keys to happiness. Every reason for one's unhappiness, anxiety and torment is ultimately lodged in one's mind. If I take charge of this reservoir of thoughts and emotions, could I experience happiness? Can it be that simple? And if it is, why can't I do it? Knowing and accepting the transiency of my life perhaps is the key to enjoying what is here right now — and becoming happy.

I sat in silence for a while and tried to imagine this possibility. I felt hopeful. I turned the radio on and listened to some soothing Japanese music, then went back to the teachings of Buddha:

"My end is approaching, your parting is near... but do not lament... life is ever changing; none can escape. Do not lament, but realize that nothing is permanent, and learn from the emptiness of human life. Buddha is not a human body... it is enlightenment. A human body must die, but wisdom will exist forever !"[21]

I turned out the lights and tried to catch some sleep, but Buddha's simple yet profound words kept me tossing and turning. They kept echoing in my mind, over and over. These are not strange territories, only appearances are strange. These words of the great Buddha I certainly have visited before in other forms and in other lands. They all seemed in unison and harmony with other familiar thoughts: Aristotle's *"There is no virtue, but intelligence;"* Descartes' *"I think, therefore I am;"* Camus' *"The world is absurd, and I am leaving it too fast."* These Greek and French ideas seemed to reconcile with the last teaching of Buddha!

We all live and toil on the same earth, sweat and labor under the same sun, gaze and wonder at the same stars. Regardless of where we are on this planet, we share the same fate. Our dress may vary, our customs may seem strange to each other — but these are superficial barriers. The human dilemma is universal, human thoughts and needs are similar, and humanity's destiny is one.

Curiously, I now felt less alienated here in Japan, *"The land of the rising sun."* I finally went to sleep.

When I awoke, the morning sun was flooding my room. It felt warm and reassuring. I stretched luxuriously and looked forward to living another day.

Simple

My Japanese friend Nakamura and I walk uphill on a balmy and partially sunny afternoon. The temperature is pleasant enough to make the walk an agreeable experience. Trees around us are swaying in the gentle afternoon breeze. The air is fresh and slightly damp. We pass through a high gate leading to the famed Zen temple of Kamakura, and wander around the manicured grounds of this magnificent shrine. Elaborate and ornate carvings decorate every beam of the wooden structure. We learn that the temple is eight centuries old.

Behind the main temple stands another large wooden structure designed in the traditional Japanese style. A lush and beautifully planned garden surrounds a small and tranquil pond behind the wooden building. The Zen Master himself has created this pond in the shape of the Japanese character signifying "Mind."

The garden serves as a sanctuary for quiet meditation and contemplation. It is a peaceful haven away from the crowds, the noise and bustle of Tokyo. I feel an inexplicable sense of identity with this peaceful place. We sit for a while on the terrace of the old structure. The gentle summer breeze is cool and comforting and the sound of wind chimes is soothing. Simply gazing at the "mind" pond brings peace to my heart.

My mind wanders to the book I read the night before… I am still captivated by its simplicity and profound wisdom. It was written around 1500 by Musashi, an extraordinary man: a Samurai, a professional soldier, a swordsman of the first degree, and a warrior who killed without hesitation. The Samurai class was considered to be the highest class in the Japanese old culture. The sword was Musashi's profession and his way of life. In that culture and at that juncture "The way of the sword" was synonymous with nobility. Samurai military art became the highest form of study inspired by Zen, which went hand-in-hand with the art of war. Perhaps Musashi came to a place like this to learn and to contemplate life's simplicity.

This traditional professional soldier was also a talented poet, painter and wisdom seeker — a contrasting mixture of talents which is portrayed in one small book titled *The Book of Five Rings.* He was writing about war and the art of combat, but indirectly he was also outlining a philosophy of life and a system of ethics: how to deal with life and how to live it, how to face the inevitability of death and accept it, how to deal with whatever life presented you. He wrote of nobility, courage, poise and self control, using the simple analogy of the warrior's craft.

The breeze suddenly intensifies and turns into a brisk wind. Clouds gather above, move around and take different shapes in a rapid progression. The new shapes change the angles of light in this tranquil garden. The trees shake and sway and begin to sound like a wild sea. Colorful leaves fly around and land on the surface of the small pond. I pause a while to watch the temperamental display. It is as if nature is reminding me that change is always in the wind and nothing is permanent.

I go back to thinking of the book I read. Musashi answered an eternally perplexing question: How does one deal with death?

"If you become accustomed to the idea of death, resolved on death, and consider yourself a dead body, you can pass through life with no possibility of failure... When you sacrifice your life, you must make the fullest use of all your weapons... It is useless to die with a weapon still

undrawn."[22] These are simple and direct truths. They blossom out of the Zen simplicity.

I walk around the grounds once more. My mind is preoccupied with thoughts evoked by these words… I feel a compelling urge to know more about Zen. I want to understand every subtle word Musashi wrote. Here I am in the midst of the most enduring shrine of Zen, this old temple with its huge bell, and surrounded by dozens of monks. If I cannot find the answer here, where else can it be found?

To understand "The way of the sword" I have to comprehend what Zen is. Nakamura takes me to the Zen Master, and I pose the question. He answers in a soft voice: *"The essence of Zen is that Knowledge is a full circle: The end point is the beginning and the highest virtue is Simplicity."*

"What does this mean?" I ask.

"You must focus your attention on reality itself, not on your intellectual and emotional reaction to it… One has to become neutral, transparent or almost void so that one's emotions do not get in the way, or one's thoughts distract from seeing the simple reality," he explains.

"It's easy for you to say. For me, my feelings and my thoughts always get in the way," I say laughingly. His response was calm and gentle: *"To focus on simple reality, without emotions or intellectual reactions, requires patience, discipline, and practice to control your mind."*

Zen does not contain any elaboration — only simplicity, I come to understand. It aims directly at the true nature of things without complications or fanfare. Zen has no ceremonies, no rules, no specific teachings. The prize of Zen is purely personal. It does not even require a change in behavior. It only requires an understanding and a change in attitude towards the nature of everyday life and death.

Zen is based on practice and personal experience with reality at the most direct and basic level. Zen does not permit theories or symbols to stand between reality and the perceiver. Buddhist monks practice mental exercises that baffle, excite, puzzle, and exhaust the mind. They do this until each realizes the simple reality of everything.

Buddha said, *"Man suffers because of his craving to possess and keep forever things that are essentially impermanent, and chief among them is his own self."*[23]

How true and how simple.

Reality is not static, it is ever-changing, ever-growing. It will never stop for an instant so we can fit it into any rigid structure. It will not wait for us to theorize about it or attach to it our own emotional stamp. Our craving to keep life stable and predictable, so we can analyze it, is an attempt to stop the waves from rushing to the shore.

I walk down the hill and watch the sun setting. I try not to focus on my own thoughts or my feelings, but rather on the flaming red disc sliding down the horizon and changing the day into night. I feel integrated with this wonderful universe and begin to understand the simplicity of it all. Nakamura smiles in silence as he senses the dawn of my enlightenment.

Sanctuary

AT MAMA NOMURI'S

Rain drops splash softly on the windshield, as our car follows the twists and the turns of the narrow roads. We are traveling the short distance from Lake Kawagouchi to Lake Yamanaka at the foot of Mount Fuji. I open the side window to catch a glimpse of the surroundings. The hills are dressed in vivid colors, for it is autumn and the leaves are changing colors to red, purple, and gold. Fog shrouds the hills like a white veil wrapped around a beautiful and curvaceous woman. The scene is both peaceful and moving: it brings back sweet memories of lovely Indian Summers in New England, where I lived for a number of years. The drive relaxes me and enchants my heart.

Despite the rain and fog, the temperature is warm. People are everywhere trying to enjoy the precious hours of the weekend. Most are hoping to enjoy a short reprieve from their intense work schedules, the traffic jams, and the crowded streets of Japan's cities. At the foot of Mount Fuji and around the beautiful lakes, the pace is always slower, the breeze is sweeter, and life is more serene.

My mind wanders back to the night before. It went all too fast— like a short and pleasant dream. The resort hotel was small, modern, designed with a Mediterranean flair. The room was elegant with its contemporary sky-blue and egg-white decor. It had a panoramic window with a spectacular view of Mount Fuji which stood in the distance in perfect symmetry — imposing, majestic. A white blanket of snow covered the entire mountain, in contrast with the evening's purple-blue sky. I became more comfortable with Japan, and my initial feelings of alienation started to melt away. The evening simply evaporated. I ate in my room, facing the window and the view... The French wine tasted like nectar, the traditional Japanese music was soothing, and when the light of my two white candles faded, I simply fell asleep.

Morning came too quickly... I rushed to the window to catch a glimpse of the mountain in the daylight. It was simply not there. Mount Fuji had disappeared, hidden by thick clouds and a dense fog which drew a gray curtain over it, erasing it from sight — like a dream that is half real, one cannot be certain whether it existed in reality, or only in one's wild imagination. The missing mountain and the cloudy sky left a bitter taste in my soul. I felt forlorn and became quiet and withdrawn, but for some reason not totally depressed. I wanted to get out and let the sudden rain wash away my old confusion and regrets. An urgent need for inner-peace and solitary contemplation was running through me. I wanted to let my soul depart and hide away in those hills, among the colorful trees, in between the rain drops. I needed to recapture the peace I felt in the temple's garden.

My Japanese friend Noriko invited me for a traditional Japanese dinner. We drove through the rain along a narrow and winding road for a while. We came upon a small restaurant in a wooden house with a straw roof, nestled neatly among colorful trees. We ran through the rain to the house and removed our soaking shoes. On the door I saw a simple sign in Japanese. My friend read it :

"*Mama Nomuri*," which means Mother Nature.
"How appropriate," I said.

As we walk into the house a sudden feeling of warmth fills me. I start to feel comfortable once again. The owner is a kind man with silvery hair and an engaging smile. He offers us hot tea, while we wait for a table. It is amazing how small things can make a great difference. The warm house, gentle people and quietness make me relax and feel at home. I notice that everybody is quiet or softly whispering — even children. No harsh noises or distracting sounds, no dishes clattering, no waiters shouting, only the pleasant sound of quiet. I fall in love with the feeling this place creates within me.

Finally our table is ready. I sit facing a large glass window. It is still raining, and the wind is moving the fog all over the scene. Outside the window, yellow, purple, red and brown leaves are scattered on the wooden deck where a few rustic tables are surrounded by blocks of wood which serve as chairs. The hills slope down to the edge of the lake, their slopes dotted with trees of many shapes and sizes.

The food is unfamiliar, yet it tastes good; I only recognize some kind of soup and fish. A mini-version of the tea ceremony interests me, but most of all I savor the special chestnut dessert.

Bit by bit I grow closer to this culture. I start to discover subtle dimensions that were not readily clear at first glance. This is the quiet, contemplative, and peaceful side of Japan. I find peace here… I come to realize that in the final analysis, home is simply where the heart is warm, the mind at peace, and the body is out of the rain.

Then again, I remember reading an excerpt from *The Dialogue of Buddha and the Shepherd*. Buddha said :

> *"I no longer need food or milk.*
>
> *The winds are my shelter, my fire is out.*
>
> *And you, sky, can rain as much as you please!*

I have neither oxen, nor cows,

I have no meadows.

I have nothing. I fear nothing.

And you, sky, can rain as much as you please!

I have a free and docile soul

For years I have trained it;

I have taught it to play with me.

And you, sky, can rain as much as you please!" [24]

Outside our window, the fog dances around the landscape, moving swiftly with the shifting wind. It hides the hills and the trees on the other side of the lake. The view fades away, then suddenly comes back in focus again and again… it allows the other side to reveal its breathtaking colors, then once more hides seductively in a shroud of white mist.

Leaving the little wooden house at night feels like abandoning a comfortable nest. It is surprising to feel this way; feelings confuse me and make me wonder. I try to understand the reasons, to search my soul for an answer. I become withdrawn again. My friend drives me back to Tokyo. The trip back to the big, crowded city is depressing. The traffic is creeping along in slow motion. I feel confined, almost trapped, and depressed; realizing that this is the time to return to harsh reality — time to face the crowds — time to leave the gentle charm. But my soul needs to retrieve the calm of the inner sanctuary…

FROM COLOSSUS TO NOTHINGNESS

Myth

F R O M   C O L O S S U S   T O   N O T H I N G N E S S

R H O D E S ,   G R E E C E   1 9 9 3

Here I am once again back in Greece. Two eventful, draining and breathless decades have passed with the speed of light. Life moved on and battle scars of time changed everything: countries, people, friends, and even the feelings within me.

On my way to Egypt for a brief visit, I stopped on the island of Rhodes to see a dear friend from youthful days in Ismailia. We always kept in touch despite oceans, preoccupations, and years that separated us.

Rhodes is a quiet, picturesque and small island located at the far eastern side of the Mediterranean, close to the coast of Turkey. It is full of ancient ruins from a succession of civilizations and cultures that invaded the island across millennia: Greeks, Romans, Christian Crusaders, Arabs and Turks, all of whom left traces and fingerprints on the face of this strategic island. Each in turn vanished, leaving behind interesting monuments: decaying pillars, maimed statues, abandoned castles. Nothing but crumbling remnants now serve as tourist attractions. They tell tales of people who lived, conquered, built monuments, then simply faded into oblivion.

In spite of this, life continues to renew itself on this island. Out of decaying rocks red, yellow, and white flowers burst defiantly… Out of the caressing sea fresh fish flow to dinner tables. In the hills, glorious sun ripens grapes for wine. People of Rhodes come out of their white-washed little homes to welcome the tourists with warmth and sincerity.

In the stillness of an early morning I linger at the edge of the harbor, near an old church with limestone walls, and survey the scene. The sea breeze is fresh and crisp. The sun is shining brilliantly; it shimmers on the blue waters and warms my spirit. The harbor is serenely quiet this early morning and the day looks promising.

Fortunately, this is not the tourist season; everything is calm, peaceful, and allows me to indulge a lazy pace. Across the harbor stands an ancient fortress. It may have been built by Arabs who occupied this island one time or another. In the water, at the foot of the ancient fortress, a modern, white luxurious yacht is docked. I find the sharp contrast amusing and somehow appealing.

On each side of the harbor entrance stands a pillar with a statue of a red deer on top. This is to mark where, as the legend goes, a giant statue of the Greek Sun-God Helios stood centuries ago. The huge statue was in the shape of a man standing astride the harbor's entry. Some storytellers claim that the statue formed an arch wide and tall enough to allow ships to sail underneath. Others claim that the statue never straddled the harbor entrance but rather stood beside it. But again, that too, is a tantalizing myth. I try to visualize how huge it must have been. I could not quite imagine it, nor fathom how it could have been constructed in such an era.

The Colossus of Rhodes disappeared, to the point where no one knows for sure if it ever existed. Unconfirmed stories claim the the statue had fallen in an earthquake, and later the invading Arabs broke it into pieces and melted its metal to make cannons. Nobody knows for sure.

I wonder to myself: Was it all a myth? Was it a figment of people's imaginations? How can something so great and so enormous melt away with no trace? How could human memory be so vague? Is everything on earth so fragile and transient? Must things have a physical, enduring existence in order to have a lasting impact? If the memories of such a

colossus are that ethereal, then how can a frail, insignificant, mortal
being last in the memory of time? How can he keep his thoughts, his
passions, and his creations from turning into nothingness?

The next day my friend and I drove up a tortuous mountain road,
listening to taped songs from the old days of Ismailia. It was another
sunny, warm, and glorious winter day. We stopped at the edge of a cliff
and I strolled closer to the platform overlooking a large lagoon. Down at
the water's edge, I saw the beautiful village of Lindos with its imposing
ancient castle thrusting out of the rocky hills. Its walls blended
harmoniously with the colors of the earth around it, forming oneness
among castle, hills and soil. Small white homes clustered together and
clung to the treeless hills surrounding the castle. Wild red poppies, white
daisies and purple pansies splashed their colors on a rugged landscape
dotted with rocks.

We drove down to the village, then strolled around its small alleys
which twisted and turned up the hill. Picturesque white-painted stone
bungalows and small shops lined the path all the way up to the castle.
Huge rock boulders had rolled down to the beach and into the water,
challenging the rushing waves.

We had lunch in the shade of an ancient grape vine, on the terrace
of a small tavern on the beach. We ate broiled fresh fish and shared a
bottle of delicious local white wine. I was impressed by the way in which
the decaying past and the lively present existed side by side, and created
such unusual beauty. The village of Lindos' charm is simply a blending
contrast of emerging youth and decaying past. Here we were, my friend
and I, blending memories of here and now with the old days of our
younger years.

The people of the island are mostly a mixture of Greek
Christian Orthodox and Moslem Turks. They live with each other in a
curious mixture of suspicion and tolerance, keeping their myopic cultural

divisions alive. They are a reflection of the realities of our human weakness and our human greatness — most of the time tolerating each other and continuing to interact in a pragmatic way.

On the last day of my visit we went to the Turkish side of the Island and dined in a Turkish restaurant by the sea. The food was exquisite and the wine delectable. We sat for hours, exploring sweet memories of the past, realities of the present, and hopes and dreams of tomorrow; amazed at the blazing pace of time, and the pain of old scars. We suddenly confront these realities when we encounter a friend we have not seen for twenty years. In a swift moment, we feel the physical passage of the years. We discover the changes in ourselves in their eyes. We feel the real wear and tear of the runaway years.

Can we stop time from rolling on? Can we ever freeze it and keep it? Can we recapture the magical moments of our happy times? Can we bring them back and turn the clock backwards? No, it is simply impossible, and it is also sad. The moments we enjoyed, even that day, all too soon became another memory in the flowing sea of time.

How can I keep this life from fading away? How can I keep my love alive in the hearts of people I love if I have to leave them? How can I create a colossus of a sort to keep me in their thoughts? How can the insignificant and mortal become significant?

Is it through our children that we continue to survive?

"Our children are not really our children," wrote Khalil Gibran. *"They are the children of life longing for itself."*[25] They are themselves and not mere extensions of us. They are individuals with their own thoughts and dreams. They will live in a world we cannot imagine even in our wildest dreams. They are not here merely to carry out our thoughts and ideals, they have their own. It is only by a divine chance that they may come to see anything the way we see it.

Perhaps the only thing left for us is creative art. It could be something more lasting and more enduring than ourselves. Perhaps we should carve a statue, paint a picture, compose a piece of music that will outlive our limited human existence. Perhaps...

My plane was vibrating on the runway that stretches along the golden beach. The wind was brisk and the sun was in its glory. It was time to say goodbye to the beautiful island, to the good friends, and then fly away.

I boarded all too soon. The plane ascended rapidly into the clear blue sky. It soared along with my spirit, circling around the island and over the old harbor, now just another memory. Suddenly, in the cabin I heard a small boy shouting to his mother: "I see it... I see it... the Colossus is down there in deep water... I can really see it!"

I smiled quietly to myself, closed my eyes and tried to imagine it.

God

The massive pillars of the temple of Karnak stand strong, proud and enduring, despite the passage of centuries. They stand in defiance of the decay and disintegration of everything around them. Here on the banks of the Nile thousands of years ago kings, priests, and an entire population worshipped one god — Ra. You can see their traces and fingerprints carved in the stone walls. You can almost hear their chants in the whispers of the winds that dance through this ancient shrine.

Across the wide, golden river and deep into the desert sand, stretches the Valley of the Kings. Here, kings, queens, and nobles of ancient Egypt are laid to rest. The place looks majestic and mysterious under the golden rays of the setting sun. It is the end of another hot day in the eternal sea of sand.

Ancient Egyptians lived, traded and worshipped on the Nile's eastern bank, where the sun rises. But, they crossed the river and buried their dead on the western bank, where the sun sets. This ritual symbolized the journey of life: sunrise meant birth, new life and new beginning; sunset meant death and an end to the first journey. They believed that life comes full circle to yet another beginning.

The Egyptians thought of and articulated the idea of one God as an eternal being above all else, before the Greeks, before Moses, Jesus, and Mohammed. They believed that one Being alone is responsible for creation. They saw the supreme god Ra, as the protector of everything in nature including the human race. The symbol of Ra is the disc of the sun, with its rays reaching out, nurturing, warming, and giving life to everything on earth.

I walk around the ancient grounds, wide-eyed, with a quivering heart and a racing mind. My thoughts switch back and forth between the way of life that existed thousands of years ago, and life as I now see it and endure it. Everything has lived, changed, decayed, and died. Humanity discovered, invented and conquered a great deal. Yet, one thing remains mysterious, ever-present and ever-perplexing: the idea of God. What is God? Who is God? Does God really exist?

When I was a child I used to lie on my back on the roof of my father's house, and look up to the sky, searching for God. "Where is He?" I asked myself. I looked desperately in the cloud formations to see if I could discover His face. I whispered to myself, "Why is He hiding from me? What does He look like?"

When I became a teenager I wondered about religions:

Do they really come from God? Which religion should I believe? Should I follow the religion of my family? What about other religions? What about the atheist point of view? Is it true?

Are there any answers for these haunting questions?

When it comes to religion, many people simply accept the beliefs that are handed down to them. They are indoctrinated into a religion, based on beliefs and practices of the family and the clergies who surround them at birth. They submit to traditions at face value, without any questioning. They recite a holy book without understanding what is behind it. They follow the crowd, and they acquiesce to customs. Some simply go through the motions with utter hypocrisy, only to please, to conform, or to create a "favorable impression."

Others reject the idea of God altogether. They decide that God does not exist, and there is no reason to worship Him. They reject all the

arguments as nothing but man-made fantasy. They believe that there is
no heaven and no hell, and after death there is nothingness. They are
convinced that God is a human invention, created out of human
weakness, that the idea of God is an attempt to cling to something —
as people drift closer to death. So, instead of facing the hard realities
of life and death, they grasp at any straw. The idea of God is simply
a convenient straw.

Beyond those two extremes there is a third category of thinking
people to whom I am drawn closer and closer as I grow older. This
category of thinking people is focused intellectually on the concept of
God. They try to find God on their own, objectively, and in spite of
inadequate early religious conditioning.

Like them, I yearn to understand the true and pure idea of God,
without any preconceived notions, fanatic hysteria, or dogmatic
traditions; to look for answers with an open mind and extended vision;
to form my own impression by looking at the concept of God from
every possible point of view. I know that this will be an agonizing,
mind wrenching, and soul searching process — a treacherous journey
to embark upon. Yet it is the only worthy and meaningful course.

I am driven to this choice by a passion for discovery, a distaste for
fanaticism, a disdain for ethnic myopia, and an antipathy to following
the crowd.

No reasonable mind can explain the extreme religious doctrines that
spread fanatic teachings, erect barriers and prejudices between human
beings, and drive people to hate and fight each other, in the name of
"God." During the Spanish Inquisition, Catholics persecuted Protestants,
Jews, and Moslems. To this day, some Moslem extremists and some
Jewish extremists still preach hatred in the Middle East. Catholics and
Protestants somehow find it acceptable to bomb each other in Northern
Ireland. Hindus and Moslems are massacring each other in India. Ethnic

cleansing in Eastern Europe is constantly in the news. Inquisitions, Crusades, Holy Wars, Jihads, "cleansing," are all waged in the name of "God." This inhuman segregation is based upon simple differences, such as whether one group worships God on Friday, Saturday or Sunday.

I ask myself, "Is this really God's message? How could it be? How could I follow such ideas? Does believing in God in a certain way mean rejecting people who believe in God any other way?"

Instinctively, I yearn for Something higher than mortality, more pure and more perfect than this corrupt world; Something eternal, powerful, good, whose unconditional love protects all beings. I have now realized that the concept of God and the doctrines of religion are not one and the same. God has nothing to do with these man-made rituals, interpretations, and discriminatory doctrines. God is innocent of all crimes being committed in his name.

I aspire, however, to keep an open mind to objective and logical thoughts, regardless of their source, or the preconditioning of such sources. I strive to be open to the ideas of like-minded people who seek to understand and search for God on their own. I must look at God from various angles.

On summer nights in Greece, I used to look up in the clear sky and see the stars brilliantly shining, in awe of the unknown force that energizes, orchestrates, and makes things move about this expanding universe: this perpetual motion of earth, stars, galaxies, and of the matter even within our own being. Who and what causes it?

Aristotle, the Greek philosopher, provides an answer:

"God is a prime mover unmoved... God does not create but rather moves the world as the lover moves the beloved object."[26] I liked this idea: God is the cause and power source of this expansive universe.

As a young boy in school, I used to wonder about this physical world with its intricate and harmonious laws and beauty, all these laws of

Physics and Biology and Chemistry: who engineered it, perfected it put it together, and keeps it going?

All that science has achieved is the discovery that these laws exist, period! It may have progressed a few steps further and exploited those laws for the benefit or the harm of mankind. Scientists smashed the atom, traveled in space, and did some genetic engineering; they certainly can prove, illustrate, use, and talk about the laws of nature. Some even claim to be experts in nuclear physics or cosmology. But, no one knows why these laws exist, how they were designed or who or what created them.

Later on in life, I read Spinoza — the 15th century Portuguese-Jewish Rabbi and philosopher who was excommunicated from his synagogue for daring to be different — who provided an answer that made some sense to me: *"God is the immanent cause of all things... The universal laws of nature and the eternal decrees of God are one and the same thing... God is the sum of all causes and all laws, and the sum of all minds."* [27]

My attempt as a child to search the clouds for a picture of a human face is a perfect example of our human incapability of perceiving God. I was searching for a kind old human face with a white beard. I imagined God's face, however, to be so huge that it could cover the whole sky.

When I entered Ismailia high school, I used to wonder: Is everything in this universe purely physical and material? Is everything readily seen, felt, heard, tasted, and touched? Or are there things beyond the capabilities of our senses?

In high school, I read in the writings of Al-Ghazzali, the Islamic thinker: *"God in his essence is one without partner, single without any similar... God is not a body possessing form, nor substance possessing bounds."* [28]

Slowly, I started to comprehend that the nature of God must be unlike that of any other being. Any power capable of controlling all of the vast universe, according to these intricate laws, must be boundless and unique. It is no wonder that God is not readily discernible. How can we perceive something without any bounds, something without any shape? How can we comprehend something absolutely unlike anything we can see, touch and feel?

When I attended Ain Shams University in Cairo, I was highly impressed by the writings of Dr. Moustapha Mahmood, the contemporary Egyptian philosopher and physician, who influenced me a great deal and introduced me to the world of philosophy. He wrote that God belongs to another order of existence.

Mahmood posed more questions: *"Am I only a body with a collection of physical needs? Is my mind nothing more than the brain cells that control the bio-functioning of my body? Is my personality only a collection of reactions and responses? Are my passions nothing other than the expression of my physical needs?"*[29]

He concluded: Each of us experiences the existence of a continuous "deep-self" — unchanging, ever-present and independent of our physical body. Our physical body changes continuously with the passage of time, but this deep-self never changes. When we encounter situations where we give no regard to death, and act as if death does not enter into our calculations, we are thinking and acting from that deep-self. This deep-self is what some call the Spirit. The Spirit does not recognize death because it is simply out of its realm. Death is an issue for the body to contend with, but not the spirit.

During the war in the Middle East I came close to death a few times. Each time, I felt I was observing myself from a point outside my body — with awe — as I acted and reacted to danger and calamity. I was surprised and overwhelmed by the degree of detachment I had experienced. I witnessed myself doing deeds as if I was watching a character in a motion picture. This happened to me once again, later in life, as I experienced a heart attack. From a very calm, detached, and higher space, I was watching my body lying on the operating table with the doctors and nurses surrounding me, and the instruments of the operating room beeping. I was not at all afraid… I did not feel any pain. I was only observing with a detached and serene curiosity.

These experiences convinced me that there is indeed another order of reality. It is an unseen and nonphysical order. If I can understand and accept the existence of a nonphysical Spirit, I can begin to come closer to understanding the nonphysical nature of God.

Moustapha Mahmood concluded that the nature of God is analogous to the nature of the Spirit. *"The Spirit is higher and more supreme than the physical body, as is God who is supreme and higher than the physical world."* [30]

My own impression of God has slowly taken shape: God must be an all-powerful and creative artist who composed the symphony of this universe, who engineered and orchestrated this colossal and elaborate production. God must be the designer, painter, sculptor, who used the same atoms as his raw materials to produce all these beautiful and breathtaking works of art that surround us. God must be the Being, who I instinctively yearn for to free me from this limited world: a Being mightier than any mortal, purer and more perfect than this world; a loving and eternal Being who is the power, the cause and the law behind this expanding universe. God must not be a body that is bound by form, nor a substance possessing limits. Therefore, God is not readily discernible, and belongs to another order of existence: the unseen, spiritual order.

But in the final analysis, does this God really exist? This is the most critical question of all. Is God a human fantasy, as the atheists claim? I need to know this, to search for my own answer. But, I must start from ground zero, where everything is doubtful, nothing is taken for granted. I shall start from the same vantage point as Descarte's. I need to set aside the teachings which demand me to take a leap of faith.

But why Descartes? For the simple reason that he expressed contempt for all education and dogmas that existed in his time. He was the ultimate revolutionary skeptic. He looked upon the thought processes of his era as outmoded, and retarded by submission to church authority. He dismissed all accumulation of life-long beliefs, and used reason and logic as the bases for believing in anything.

Descartes doubted even his own senses. True, our vision does not see things that can be depicted by microscopes; our hearing does not pick up the radio waves without the help of a radio receiver, and we are deceived by such phenomena as optical illusions.

Descartes doubted the existence of material things because they are based upon sense perceptions. Sciences must be doubted for basically the same reason. *"The only thing we can trust,"* said Descartes, *"is our logical conclusions… which we can reach by reason, not by the senses."*[31]

Descartes wanted to start from a concrete point, a point that cannot be ever doubted. He finally found it and arrived at his most significant conclusion: *"Even if I am deceived by my own logic, I must exist in order to be deceived. If I doubt all my beliefs there is only one belief I cannot doubt: I must exist to doubt. I think, therefore I am. (Je pense, donc je suis.)"*

From that very point Descartes embarked upon a quest to answer the question of God's existence. He began by asserting three basic facts:

> *"- There must be as much reality in the cause as in its effects;*
>
> *- Something cannot proceed from nothing;*
>
> *-What is perfect cannot proceed from the less perfect."*[32]

On the basis of these three facts he concluded:

"I could not have caused the idea of God because I am only a finite and imperfect being, whereas the idea of God is of a perfect and infinite being. Something else, greater than I, must have caused that idea. Therefore, God exists as the only possible cause of my idea of him."

Descartes added another argument: *"Existence belongs to the nature of God as a perfect being. If God lacked existence, he would be less perfect. But God (by definition) has no imperfections; therefore God must exist."* [33]

When I moved on to America, I wanted to learn more. I read some writings by Thomas Aquinas, the Catholic theologian, who also tried to prove God's existence by rational arguments. He wrote: *"Since every thing in the world has a cause, there must be a first cause, in a series of causes. This first cause is God... the harmony, orderliness and beauty of physical nature by which humanity is provided with suitable temperature, light, food, water, shelter, and aesthetic delight could not be accidental. It must be planned by an intelligent being. God exists as the necessary designer, planner and governor of the universe."* [34]

Taking all these thoughts together, and mixing them with my own experiences, impressions, and logical conclusions, I have come to the following summation:

I am sitting here thinking, searching and wondering.
I must exist to think and put these thoughts on paper.
Since I am here, something must have caused me to exist.

I have found that I possess a "deep-self" that is ever-present, and unchanging, despite the passage of time.

It acts from a higher plane beyond my physical body.
It observes my life as one watches a motion picture.
It proves to me the existence of another order of reality:
the unseen order.

I need not doubt the existence of people around me, who
love or hate me. They are in my face every day. How can
I doubt their existence? Even if I try, they would not
allow me such a luxury. Therefore, others exist sometimes
to my delight, sometimes to my chagrin.

I accept the physical world and all the scientific
discoveries that explain and exploit it. There is no need
for me to doubt it, especially when I benefit from all its
fruits. It obviously does exist and it is wonderful.

This physical world shares a unity of the basic elements
and their atoms. All forms of life, whether plant or
animal, have been built from a combination of carbon,
hydrogen and oxygen. This indicates the existence of the
same artist, designer and engineer who used these media
according to precise laws.

The harmony and beauty of physical nature by which
humanity is provided with amenable conditions could not
be accidental. It must have been planned by an intelligent
and powerful Being.

Despite all our sophistication and scientific advances, we know very little about the Cosmos. Science cannot yet determine whether or not there was a Big Bang, and if there was one, what caused it. Scientists cannot assert or deny the existence of matter before the Big Bang, nor the exact time it took place. Theoretically, all they can tell us is that it is probable that the Big Bang may have occurred some billions of years ago. Science can analyze a living cell and describe the chemical composition within it, but it cannot recreate it... There must be an unseen power beyond material Science's comprehension that caused this life to exist.

Finally, what are these intuitive perceptions, this instinctive drive that prompted me, a non-religious man, to go on searching, pondering. What has driven me to this?

One can make only one logical conclusion: there must be an intelligent, unseen power that exists as the cause of all. This power is God.

Then if God exists, what is his point? Why do the innocent suffer? Why do the young die? Why do we have to languish in pain, injustice and stupidity?

The questions continue on and on. There is still so much I do not know.

Song

O F   A   S T R A N G E R

This heart that pulsates within me
in pain,
in joy,
all day,
and all night
I know exists ...

This world
I see,
touch,
enjoy,
and endure
I know exists ...

But, there ends my certitude.

This genesis
agony,
exodus,
nobility,
and vulgarity

This life,
beauty,
frailty,
absurdity,
and death
are contradicting aspects
I cannot reconcile ...

This heart,
this world,
this life
are inexplicable to me

Eternally, I remain a stranger
And yet remain passionate
in my love for life
in my search for truth

S A R   R A M A D A N

[1, 2, 3] Durant, Will, <u>The Story Of Philosophy</u>, 1926.

[4, 5] Kazantzakis, Nikos, <u>Zorba The Greek</u>, 1952.

[6, 7] Christian, James L., Philosophy, <u>An Introduction To The Art Of Wondering</u>,1927.

[8] Fitzgerald translation, Edward, <u>Rubaiyat Of Omar Khayyam</u>, 11th Century.

[9] Christian, James L., <u>Philosophy, An Introduction To The Art Of Wondering</u>, 1927.

[10] Long, George, <u>The Meditations Of Marcus Aurelius</u>, 168.

[11] Camus, Albert, <u>Le Mythe De Sisyphe</u>, (In French) 1942, by Libraire Gallimard.

[12] Christian, James L., <u>Philosophy, An Introduction To The Art Of Wondering</u>,1927.

[13] Gibran, Khalil, <u>The Prophet</u>, 1923.

[14] Spinoza, Baruch, <u>The Ethics</u>, 1677, translated by Samuel Shirley, Copyright 1982 by Hackett Publishing co.

[15] Feynman, Richard P., <u>Six Easy Pieces</u>, 1963, copyright by California Institute of Technology.

[16] Fitzgerald translation, Edward, <u>Rubaiyat Of Omar Khayyam</u>,11th Century. Barnes & Noble Books 1993.

[17] Servan-Schreiber, Jean-Louis, <u>The Return Of Courage</u>, 1937.

[18] Musashi, Miyamoto, <u>A Book Of Five Rings</u>, translated and copyrights by Victor Harris 1974.

[19-21] Kyokai, Bukkyo Dendo, <u>The Teaching Of Buddha</u>,

[21] 1966.

[22] Watts, Alan, <u>The Spirit Of Zen</u>, 1958.

[23, 24] Kyokai, Bukkyo Dendo, <u>The Teaching Of Buddha</u>, 1966.

[25] Gibran, Khalil, <u>The Prophet</u>, 1923.

[26, 27] Durant, Will <u>The Story Of Philosophy</u>, 1926.

[28] The Islamic Center, Washington D.C. <u>The Five Pillars Of Islam</u>.

[29, 30] Mahmood, Moustafa, <u>My Trip From Doubt To Certitude</u> (in Arabic), 1977.

[31-34] Encyclopaedia Britannica, Inc. <u>Great Books Of The Western World – Syntopicon</u>.

O R D E R F O R M

RaMar Company
2431 Palisades Crest, Lake Oswego, OR 97034

Impressions, by Sar Ramadan

Please send me _____ copies @ $20.00 each $_____

Shipping and handling in U.S.A. ($3.00/copy)   _____

Total $_____

SHIP TO:

Name _____

Address _____

_____

Telephone_____

PAYMENT:

_____Check enclosed (*make payable to RaMar Company*)

_____Money order enclosed

_____Visa #_____exp. date _____

Signature _____

MAIL ORDER FORM TO:

RaMar Company
2431 Palisades Crest
Lake Oswego, OR 97034
USA